TEACHER'S GUIDE 3A

Noogol

Googol

Ooogol

Koogol

Toogol

Zoogol

Consultant and author
Dr Fong Ho Kheong

Authors
Chelvi Ramakrishnan and Michelle Choo

UK consultants
Carole Skinner, Simon d'Angelo and Elizabeth Gibbs

OXFORD
UNIVERSITY PRESS

© 2015 Marshall Cavendish Education Pte Ltd

Published by Marshall Cavendish Education
Times Centre, 1 New Industrial Road, Singapore 536196
Customer Service Hotline: (65) 6213 9444
Email: tmesales@mceducation.com
Website: www.mceducation.com

Distributed by
Oxford University Press
Great Clarendon Street, Oxford,
OX2 6DP, United Kingdom
www.oxfordprimary.co.uk
www.oxfordowl.co.uk

First published 2015
Reprinted 2015, 2017

ISBN 978-981-01-8883-2

Printed in the United Kingdom

Acknowledgements
Written by Dr Fong Ho Kheong, Chelvi Ramakrishnan and Michelle Choo

UK consultants: Carole Skinner, Simon d'Angelo and Elizabeth Gibbs

Cover artwork by Daron Parton

The authors and publisher would like to thank all schools and individuals who helped to trial and review Inspire Maths resources.

Contents

The background to *Inspire Maths*

A letter from Dr Fong Ho Kheong

Dear Colleague,

I am both humbled and proud to see that my work has now been adapted for use in many countries. *My Pals are Here!*, the series from which *Inspire Maths* is adapted, has been translated into languages including Spanish, Indonesian, Dutch and Arabic, and the books are used by millions of children all over the world.

International surveys show that children taught with the series score higher than their peers in standardised tests, and also that it helps young children to become more confident with maths. The 2012 PISA survey again placed Singapore's children at the top of international rankings for mathematics; the country also had the highest percentage of top achievers. In the USA, it was reported in 2013 that schools in the Fayette County, West Virginia who had adopted the programme had made impressive progress in their mathematics results, including a 12 per cent improvement among third graders in one school and a 20 per cent improvement among fourth graders in another.

Why does *Inspire Maths* work? A major strength of *Inspire Maths* is its robust structure, based on best-practice principles and methods of teaching and learning mathematics, including the concrete-pictorial-abstract (CPA) and scaffolding approaches, and a systematic teaching pathway. This comprehensive pathway emphasises mastery – with continuous, active reinforcement of concepts to help children assimilate and accommodate their learning – followed by extension, challenging children to develop and practise the thinking skills that will enable them to become confident, critically aware and independent learners. The textbooks from which *Inspire Maths* is adapted have also been informed by continuous evaluation of their success in the classroom, through a process of school visits, classroom observation and programme review. Because of this, *Inspire Maths* gives you a proven framework for supporting children of all abilities to achieve success.

Inspire Maths is based on well-established constructivist ideas of learning, and the views of internationally-renowned educationalists including Jerome Bruner, Jean Piaget, Lev Vygotsky, Richard Skemp and David Ausubel. Constructivism underpins the programme's approach to learning mathematical concepts and skills through assimilation and accommodation, and their reinforcement through reflective activities such as journal writing and error correction. This perspective is also reflected in the programme's emphasis on mastery learning and building children's confidence.

More particularly, Bruner's three modes of representation are mirrored by the concrete–pictorial–abstract learning progression which is central to *Inspire Maths*. Bruner's ideas parallel Piaget's stages of development; essentially, children's understanding of mathematical concepts depends on their stage of development. Learning in the early stages is achieved through concrete representation. Then, when ready, children can move on to pictorial representations – such as the bar model – which in turn provide them with a bridge to the abstract stage, and a flexible, fully independent understanding of the abstract, symbolic language of maths. Though it cannot be used to tackle every problem, the bar model has a particularly significant role in helping children at the concrete and semi-concrete operational stage (Piaget's developmental theory) to approach and solve problems successfully.

Skemp's ideas about instrumental and relational understanding are also an important part of the pedagogy underpinning *Inspire Maths*. Skemp suggests that learning mathematics by relating ideas to each other (relational understanding) is more meaningful, and therefore more effective, than memorising facts and procedures (instrumental understanding). Building on these ideas, *Inspire Maths* is designed to develop children's lasting and profound mathematical understanding which they will continue to extend and apply.

I would like to congratulate the UK schools and teachers who have made the choice to use *Inspire Maths*. I am confident that your children will experience similar success to that seen in other countries who have adopted this approach.

Dr Fong achieved a PhD in Mathematics Education from King's College London before teaching mathematics in the National Institute of Education, Nanyang Technological University, for over 24 years. He is currently a senior Mathematics Specialist with the Regional Centre for Education in Science and Mathematics (RECSAM) in Penang, Malaysia. He has published more than 100 journal articles, research reports, and primary and secondary mathematics books, and his research work includes diagnosing children with mathematical difficulties and teaching thinking skills to solve mathematical problems.

What is *Inspire Maths?*

Inspire Maths is the UK edition of *My Pals are Here!*, the internationally renowned approach used to teach maths in Singapore, which was heavily influenced by the Cockroft report of 1982[1]. Singapore's Ministry of Education drew on leading international research on effective teaching and learning of mathematics to meet the challenge of raising primary mathematics attainment within Singapore's schools.

The approach to mathematics teaching and learning that was developed was further refined over subsequent decades and it is this approach that is central to *My Pals are Here!* Authored by Dr Fong Ho Kheong and first published in 2001, *My Pals are Here!* is used by almost 100% of State Primary schools and over 80% of Primary schools in Singapore.

Dr Fong's overarching aim in developing *My Pals are Here!* was to help all children understand and use mathematics confidently and competently, and to support non-specialist maths teachers to deliver this. The programme's success in achieving this aim is reflected in the high levels of mathematics attainment by Singapore's pupils, who are consistently ranked among the very top in international comparison studies such as PISA and TIMSS. It is also reflected in the results of schools outside Singapore that have adopted the series, for example, in the USA and South Africa.

Inspire Maths provides a highly scaffolded learning framework with problem solving at its heart. It is built on a focused, coherent and cumulative spiral curriculum that continuously builds and consolidates knowledge to reach deep understanding. The programme encourages extensive practice to develop fluency and mastery, so that every child – across all abilities – can succeed at mathematics.

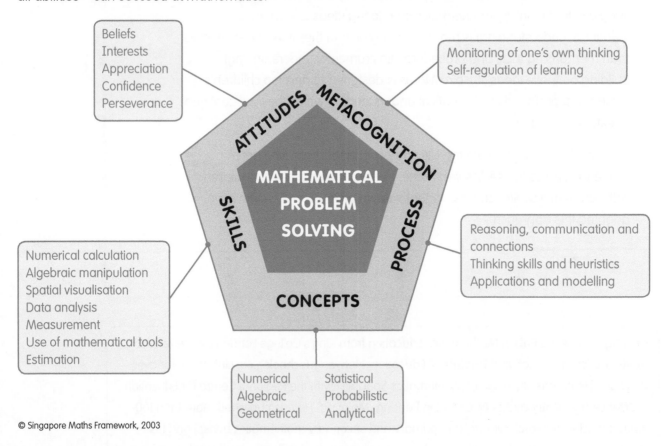

© Singapore Maths Framework, 2003

The principles that underpin *Inspire Maths*

---

1   Mathematics Counts, Dr W.H.Cockroft, 1982

The concrete-pictorial-abstract approach

Inspire Maths emphasises the development of critical thinking and problem solving skills, which help children make connections to develop deeper understanding. The powerful concrete–pictorial–abstract (CPA) approach, including the bar model method, is central to this.

Why is the CPA approach so powerful? From very early on in their school life, we expect children to use and understand numbers, which are abstract concepts. Many children struggle with this and so their first experiences of mathematics can be confusing, leaving them with no solid foundation to build on for later learning. The CPA approach helps children achieve secure number sense – that is, a sense of what numbers really represent and how to use them mathematically. This is done through a series of carefully structured representations – first using physical objects (concrete), then diagrams or pictures (pictorial), and ultimately using representations such as numerals (abstract).

In the example below from *Inspire Maths* Pupil Textbook 3A, children are exploring place value to 10 000. Using the CPA approach, they explore with base ten equipment, then using pictures of base ten alongside place value charts, and finally through words, written symbols and calculations.

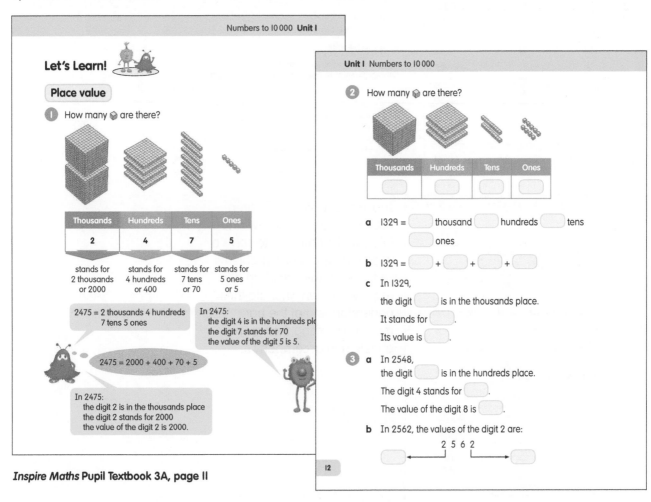

Inspire Maths **Pupil Textbook 3A, page 11**

Inspire Maths **Pupil Textbook 3A, page 12**

The bar model

The bar model is a step-by-step method that helps children to understand and extract the information within a calculation or word problem. By drawing a bar model, children translate a calculation or word problem into a picture. The approach helps children process the information given in the problem, visualise the structure, make connections and solve the problem.

The bar model is first introduced in *Inspire Maths* 2. In the following activity, children explore addition and subtraction initially with concrete apparatus before moving on to using a pictorial representation – the bar model.

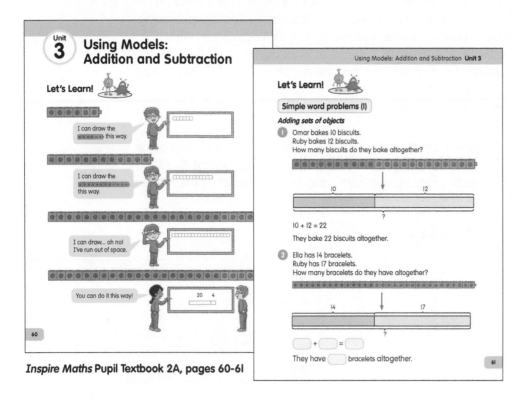

Inspire Maths **Pupil Textbook 2A, pages 60-61**

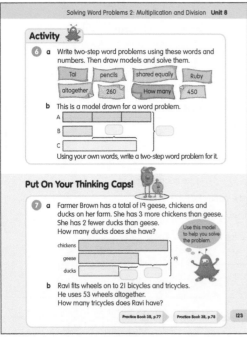

Inspire Maths **Pupil Textbook 3A, page 123**

In *Inspire Maths* 3, children are encouraged to draw and interpret bar models to solve a wide variety of word problems. In this example, children are required to demonstrate their understanding of the bar model by writing their own question to accompany it.

Heuristics for problem solving

Inspire Maths helps children learn to use *heuristics* to solve problems. *Heuristics* refers to the different strategies that children can adopt to solve unfamiliar or non-routine problems. These strategies include drawing the bar model, pattern-spotting, using diagrams and estimating or 'guess and check'.

In this example from *Inspire Maths* Pupil Textbook 3B, children are encouraged to make fraction strips to help them compare fractions.

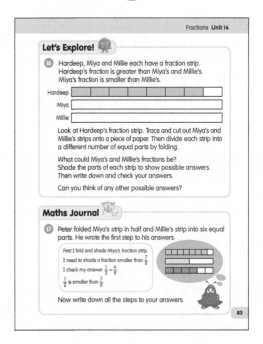

Inspire Maths **Pupil Textbook 3B, page 83**

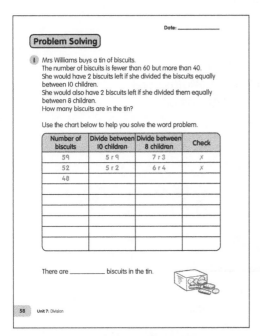

Inspire Maths **Practice Book 3B, page 58**

The *Inspire Maths* Practice Books reinforce concepts introduced in the Pupil Textbooks and provide varied, frequent practice to develop fluency. As they practise, children begin to self-select the appropriate strategy for each problem, helping them to become confident problem solvers.

Higher-order questioning

Inspire Maths is designed to stimulate thinking beyond the activities from the Pupil Textbooks. The activities should kick-start mathematically meaningful conversations through questioning, giving children opportunities to think mathematically, discover connections and be creative.

You can use written problems as a starting point for further questioning, for example, when presented with 7 + 4 = 11 and an accompanying bar model, you might ask, 'What would happen if it was 11 – 4? Or 11 – 7? What about 7 + 4 or 4 + 7?' Then take it further: 'What would the bar model look like if it was 8 + 4?'

Modelling higher-order questioning at every opportunity will encourage children to use this strategy to explore and solve problems for themselves.

Making use of variation

Research shows that mathematical and perceptual variation deepens understanding as it constantly challenges children to develop their existing understanding by looking at questions from different perspectives and adapting to new situations. The numbers and problems in *Inspire Maths* activities have been specifically selected on this basis to challenge children as the questions progress and lead them towards mastery.

Mathematical variation

With mathematical variation, the mathematical concept, for example addition, stays the same but the variation is in the mathematics. For example, addition *without* regrouping and addition *with* regrouping. The variation challenges children to use their mathematical skills flexibly to suit the situation, deepening understanding.

Perceptual variation

With perceptual variation, the mathematical concept is the same throughout the sequence of questions but is presented in different ways. In this example from *Inspire Maths* Pupil Textbook 3B, perceptual variation in fractions is provided by the use of diagrams and fraction strips alongside numerals, leading to a deeper understanding.

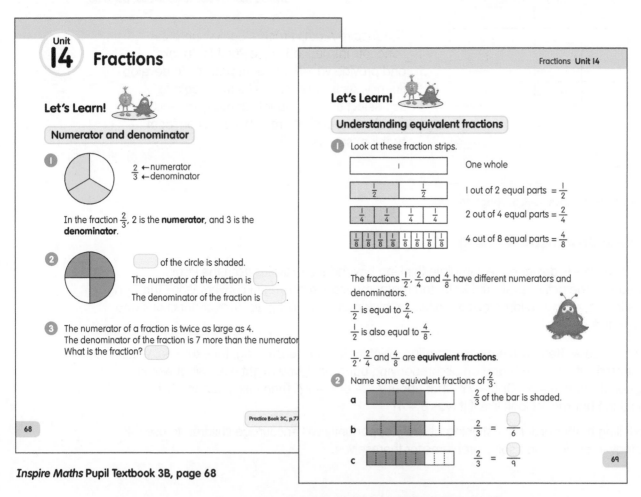

Inspire Maths **Pupil Textbook 3B, page 68**

Inspire Maths **Pupil Textbook 3B, page 69**

The *Inspire Maths* teaching pathway

Inspire Maths is a programme that teaches to mastery. It is built on a cumulative spiral curriculum, focusing on core topics to build deep understanding. The *Inspire Maths* teaching pathway scaffolds in-depth learning of key mathematical concepts through the development of problem-solving and critical thinking skills, and extensive opportunities for practice.

Pupil Textbooks to scaffold new learning

Inspire Maths Pupil Textbooks present new learning clearly and consistently, providing a highly scaffolded framework to support all children. Mathematical concepts are presented visually, with specific and structured activities, to build firm foundations. There are two Pupil Textbooks for each level.

Let's Learn! to build firm foundations

Carefully scaffolded learning through *Let's Learn!* activities in the *Inspire Maths* Pupil Textbooks promotes deep mathematical understanding through:

- clearly presented pages to illustrate how the CPA approach can be used to build firm foundations

- careful questioning to support the use of concrete apparatus

- opportunities for higher-order questioning (see page ix) to help children become confident and competent problem solvers

- opportunities to assess each child's understanding and prior knowledge through observing their use of concrete apparatus and how they approach the activity

- use of mathematical talk to explore and develop reasoning skills.

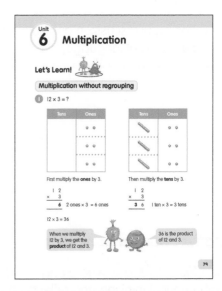

Inspire Maths Pupil Textbook 3A, page 79

Guided practice to develop deep understanding

After a concept has been introduced in *Let's Learn!*, guided practice develops the deep understanding required for mastery. Support and guide children as they work collaboratively in pairs or small groups through the guided practice activities indicated by empty coloured boxes in the Pupil Textbook.

Frequent opportunities for guided practice:

- help children develop deep understanding

- develop mathematical language and reasoning through collaborative work

- provide further opportunities to check children's understanding by observing their use of concrete apparatus and listening to their discussions

- help you to provide appropriate intervention – guiding those who need extra support and challenging those who are ready for the next step.

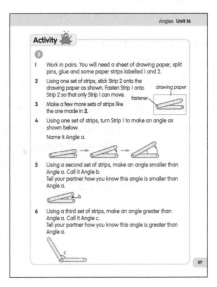

Inspire Maths Pupil Textbook 3B, page 117

Let's Explore! and *Games* to investigate and apply learning

Engaging games and investigative *Let's Explore!* activities in the *Inspire Maths* Pupil Textbooks encourage children to apply concepts they have been learning and provide an opportunity to assess their reasoning skills by observing how they approach the tasks.

Children work collaboratively in small groups or pairs:

- games reinforce skills, concepts and problem solving strategies leading to mastery

- *Let's Explore!* activities encourage children to investigate connections through mathematical reasoning

- meaningful discussion and conversation develop mathematical language.

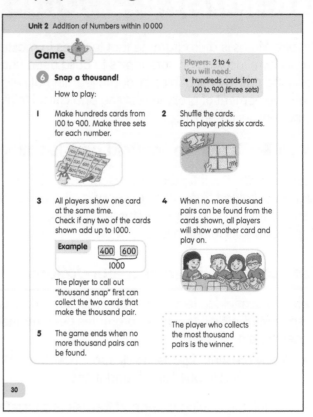

Inspire Maths Pupil Textbook 3A, page 30

Maths Journal to reflect

The *Maths Journal* is where each child records their mathematical thinking and reflects on their learning. The typical Maths Journal would be a child's own exercise book or notebook – something that the child 'owns', can share with you, with parents or carers, and that builds up over time.

Children reflect on their learning through their Maths Journal:

- giving both the child and you a valuable assessment tool, showing progress over time

- providing opportunities for children to discuss their thinking with each other, parents or carers, and with you, helping to establish next steps and giving a sense of pride in their achievements.

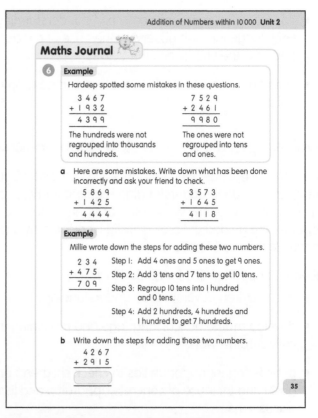

Inspire Maths Pupil Textbook 3A, page 35

Put on Your Thinking Caps! to challenge

Each unit concludes with a *Put on Your Thinking Caps!* activity in the Pupil Textbook which challenges children to solve non-routine problems.

Challenging activities:

- ask children to draw on prior knowledge as well as newly learned concepts

- ask children to use problem solving strategies and critical thinking skills, for example sequencing or comparing

- provide valuable opportunities to assess whether children have developed a deep understanding of a concept by listening to their explanations of their mathematical thinking and looking at how they model the problem, for example using concrete apparatus and pictorial representations.

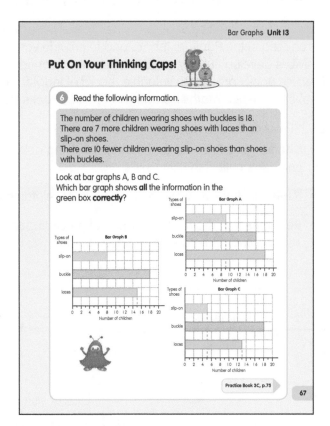

Inspire Maths Pupil Textbook 3B, page 67

Home Maths to encourage mathematical conversations

Home maths activities in the Pupil Textbooks are engaging, hands-on suggestions that parents and carers can use with children to explore maths further outside the classroom, for example through finding shapes in pictures and around the house.

Engaging home activities:

- help you to involve parents and carers in their child's mathematical learning

- help children to see maths in the world around them.

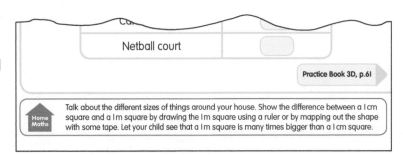

Inspire Maths Pupil Textbook 3B, page 161

Practice Books to develop fluency and consolidate

Inspire Maths Practice Books provide carefully structured questions to reinforce concepts introduced in the Pupil Textbooks and to provide varied, frequent practice. A wealth of activities develop fluency, build mathematical confidence and lead towards mastery. The Practice Books are also a valuable record of individual progress. There are four Practice Books for *Inspire Maths* 1-3 and two Practice Books for *Inspire Maths* 4-6.

Each Practice Book includes:

- **Challenging Practice** and **Problem Solving** activities to develop children's critical thinking skills

- **Reviews** after every two or three units, to reinforce learning

- **Revisions** that draw from a range of preceding topics, concepts and strands, for more complete consolidation.

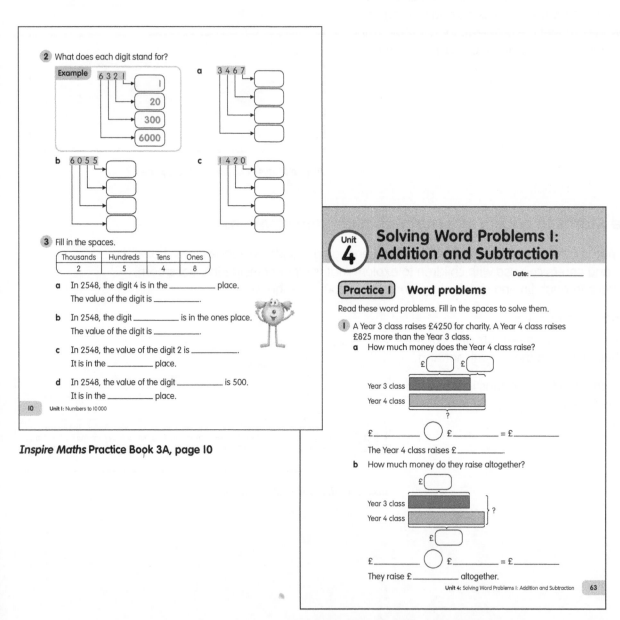

Inspire Maths **Practice Book 3A, page 10**

Inspire Maths **Practice Book 3A, page 63**

Assessment Books to create a record of progress

Inspire Maths provides comprehensive Assessment Books with regular summative assessments to create a record of progress for each child, as well as giving children opportunities to reflect on their own learning. The wraparound assessment provided through the *Inspire Maths* teaching pathway in combination with the *Inspire Maths* Assessment Books enables rapid, appropriate intervention as soon as a child needs it, before they fall behind and when they are ready to be challenged. Topics and concepts are frequently revisited in the assessments, helping to build mastery.

There is one Assessment Book for each level, providing complete coverage of the key concepts across a year. Each assessment is divided into sections so you can easily break them down into appropriate chunks to suit your class. For the early levels, you may choose to assess in small groups, reading out the questions and scribing answers. Encourage children to use concrete apparatus when they need support to help them work through the questions.

There are three types of assessment within each Assessment Book:

1. **Main assessments:** The main assessments cover the key learning objectives from the preceding two or three units of the Pupil Textbooks. Through the main assessments, children are given opportunities to apply their learning in a variety of different contexts, helping you to quickly identify which children are ready to move on and which need further support. Children may self-mark to reflect on their progress.

2. **Check-ups:** There are four check-ups for each level which revisit the previous units, drawing on prior knowledge to encourage children to make connections and apply their learning to solve problems. These assessments give you valuable opportunities to check children's understanding through observing how they approach questions, use and interpret mathematical language and use heuristics.

3. **Challenging Problems:** These assessments make use of non-routine and unfamiliar questions to see how children use their repertoire of strategies to tackle more challenging problems. Use this as an opportunity to assess children's mathematical thinking, reasoning and problem solving skills by looking at their methods and how they approach the problem. They are particularly suitable for extension and assessing a child's level of mastery.

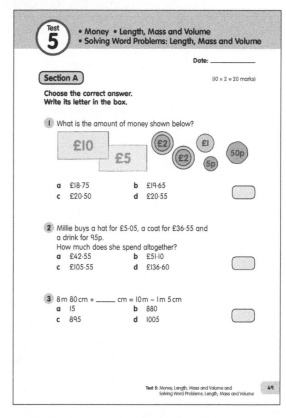

Inspire Maths Assessment Book 3, page 49

Using the Teacher's Guide

There are two *Inspire Maths* Teacher's Guides for each level, one per Pupil Textbook. Each Teacher's Guide contains:

- information on how to get started
- long-term planning support
- medium-term planning support
- suggested teaching sequence for each pupil textbook page
- answers
- photocopiable activities.

Learning objectives clearly signal the aims of the unit, which are designed to help children develop their understanding of the unit's key concepts. Children are introduced to the learning objectives in the Pupil Textbook. The Practice Book provides opportunities to practise and consolidate for mastery.

Key concepts clearly outline the important ideas children will be introduced to within each unit.

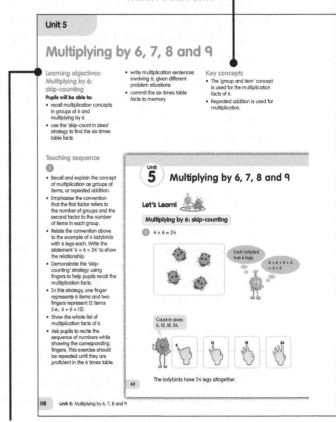

Inspire Maths **Teacher's Guide 3A, pages 118-119**

Links to the Practice Books provide opportunities for **independent work** when children are ready, to develop fluency and lead towards mastery.

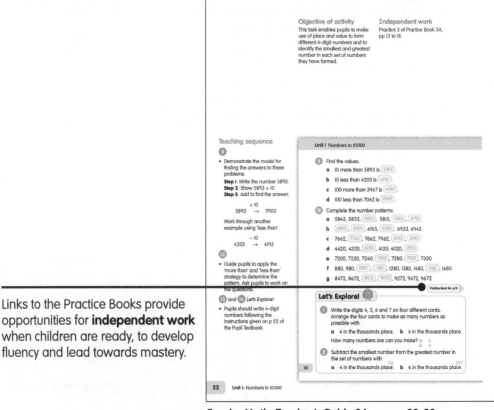

Inspire Maths **Teacher's Guide 3A, pages 22-23**

Key thinking skills and problem solving strategies
to look for and encourage are clearly highlighted, helping you to make meaningful assessments of children's understanding.

Thinking skills
- Associating
- Relating
- Identifying relationships
- Recalling
- Applying multiplication facts

Additional activity
Ask pupils to work in pairs or in groups of six. Use concrete representations to show groups of six.

Ask the class to count in sixes. '6, 12, 18, 24, 30, 36, 42, 48, 54, 60'

Pupils should look for a number pattern in the ones digits of the multiples of 6: 6, 2, 8, 4, 0, 6, 2, 8, 4, 0 ...

What you will need
- Number-train cut-outs (see Photocopy master 7 on page 267)
- Dice

Equipment needed for each Pupil Textbook page is listed to help you prepare for the activities.

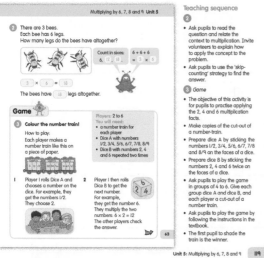

Multiplying by 6, 7, 8 and 9 **Unit 5**

② There are 3 bees.
Each bee has 6 legs.
How many legs do the bees have altogether?

Count in sixes: 6 + 6 + 6
6, 12, 18 .   = 3 × 6

3 × 6 = 18

The bees have 18 legs altogether.

Game

③ Colour the number train!

How to play:
Each player makes a number train like this on a piece of paper.

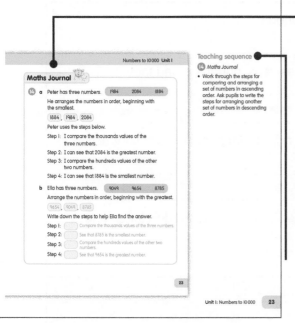

1   Player 1 rolls Dice A and chooses a number on the dice. For example, they get the numbers 1/2. They choose 2.

2   Player 1 then rolls Dice B to get the next number. For example, they get the number 6. They multiply the two numbers: 6 × 2 = 12 The other players check the answer.

Players: 2 to 6
You will need:
- a number train for each player
- Dice A with numbers 1/2, 3/4, 5/6, 6/7, 7/8, 8/9
- Dice B with numbers 2, 4 and 6 repeated two times

63

Teaching sequence

②
- Ask pupils to read the question and relate the context to multiplication. Invite volunteers to explain how to apply the concept to the problem.
- Ask pupils to use the 'skip-counting' strategy to find the answer.

③ *Game*
- The objective of this activity is for pupils to practise applying the 2, 4 and 6 multiplication facts.
- Make copies of the cut-out of a number-train.
- Prepare dice A by sticking the numbers 1/2, 3/4, 5/6, 6/7, 7/8 and 8/9 on the faces of a dice.
- Prepare dice B by sticking the numbers 2, 4 and 6 twice on the faces of a dice.
- Ask pupils to play the game in groups of 4 to 6. Give each group dice A and dice B, and each player a cut-out of a number train.
- Ask pupils to play the game by following the instructions in the textbook.
- The first pupil to shade the train is the winner.

Objective of activity
Pupils will be able to:
- express their understanding of the process of comparing and ordering numbers.
- express their understanding of place and value by listing the similarities and differences between pairs of numbers.

Additional activity
Ask pupils to work in groups of 4. Provide each group with a sequence of numbers that cannot make a number pattern. Ask pupils to rearrange the digits within the numbers so that a number pattern can be made.

Ideas for **further practice activities** to develop fluency are outlined in every unit.

Opportunities are flagged for children to work independently in their **Maths Journal**, to record and reflect on their learning, leading towards mastery.

The **teaching sequence** provides clear step-by-step guidance towards meeting the learning objectives. It highlights problem solving strategies to focus on and support for meaningful mathematical conversation and making the best use of concrete apparatus.

Numbers to 10 000 **Unit 1**

Maths Journal

⑭ a   Peter has three numbers.   1984   2084   1884

He arranges the numbers in order, beginning with the smallest.

1884 , 1984 , 2084

Peter uses the steps below.

Step 1: I compare the thousands values of the three numbers.

Step 2: I can see that 2084 is the greatest number.

Step 3: I compare the hundreds values of the other two numbers.

Step 4: I can see that 1884 is the smallest number.

b   Ella has three numbers.   9049   9654   8785

Arrange the numbers in order, beginning with the greatest.

9654 , 9049 , 8785

Write down the steps to help Ella find the answer.

Step 1: [ ] Compare the thousands values of the three numbers.

Step 2: [ ] See that 8785 is the smallest number.

Step 3: [ ] Compare the hundreds values of the other two numbers.

Step 4: [ ] See that 9654 is the greatest number.

23

Teaching sequence

⑭ *Maths Journal*
- Work through the steps for comparing and arranging a set of numbers in ascending order. Ask pupils to write the steps for arranging another set of numbers in descending order.

Long-term planning

Unit title	Key concepts
I Numbers to 10 000	
Counting	• Counting numbers up to 10 000 by using concrete representations and strategies of ones, tens, hundreds and thousands
Place value	• The digits of a number have their own values in terms of ones, tens, hundreds and thousands
Comparing, order and pattern	• Numbers up to 10 000 can be compared and arranged in ascending or descending order
2 Addition of Numbers within 10 000	
The meaning of sum	• The meaning of 'sum' is to add
Simple addition within 10 000	• Addition within 10 000 without regrouping
Addition with regrouping in hundreds	• Addition with regrouping in hundreds
Addition with regrouping in ones, tens and hundreds	• Addition with regrouping in ones, tens and hundreds
Practice Book – Review I	
Assessment Book – Test I	
3 Subtraction of Numbers within 10 000	
The meaning of difference	• The regrouping concept in subtraction
Simple subtraction within 10 000	• Subtraction without regrouping
Subtraction with regrouping in hundreds and thousands	• Regrouping from thousands to hundreds
Subtraction with regrouping in ones, tens, hundreds and thousands	• Subtraction with regrouping in ones, tens, hundreds and thousands
Subtraction with numbers that have zeros	• Regrouping from thousands to hundreds, tens and ones in subtraction
4 Solving Word Problems I: Addition and Subtraction	
Word problems	• Translating addition and subtraction concepts into models for solving two-step word problems
Practice Book – Review 2	
Practice Book – Revision I	
Assessment Book – Test 2, Challenging Problems I, Check-up I	

Unit title	Key concepts
5 Multiplying by 6, 7, 8 and 9	
Multiplying by 6: skip-counting	• The 'group and item' concept is used for the multiplication facts of 6 • Repeated addition is used for multiplication
Multiplying by 7: skip-counting	• The 'group and item' concept is used for the multiplication facts of 7 • Repeated addition is used for multiplication
Multiplying by 8: skip-counting	• The 'group and item' concept is used for the multiplication facts of 8 • Repeated addition is used for multiplication
Multiplying by 9	• The 'group and item' concept is used for the multiplication facts of 9 • Repeated addition is used for multiplication
Short cut method for multiplying by 6, 7, 8 and 9	• The relating facts concept is used to find a more difficult multiplication fact
Division: finding the number of items in each group	• Division is the inverse of multiplication • Division involves distribution of a set of items equally into some groups by relating multiplication facts
Division: making equal groups	• The 'group and item' concept in multiplication is applied • Relating multiplication and division using the 'group and item' concept is applied
6 Multiplication	
Multiplication without regrouping	• A number up to 1000 can be conceptualised as the sum of its values in the ones, tens and hundreds places • Multiplication of a 2-digit number or a 3-digit number by a 1-digit number is the sum of multiplying values from different places
Multiplication with regrouping in ones, tens and hundreds	
Multiplication with regrouping in ones, tens, hundreds and thousands	• A number up to 1000 can be conceptualised as the sum of its values in the ones, tens and hundreds places • Multiplication of a 2-digit number or a 3-digit number by a 1-digit number is the sum of multiplying values from different places • Regrouping in ones, tens, hundreds and thousands is used in multiplication
Practice Book – Review 3	
7 Division	
Quotient and remainder	• Division of a 2-digit number by a 1-digit number with remainder
Odd and even numbers	• Recognising patterns to identify odd and even numbers
Division without remainder and regrouping	• Expressing a number as a sum of values of different places • Dividing equally with no remainder

Unit title	Key concepts
Division with regrouping in tens and ones	• Expressing a number as a sum of values of different places • Dividing equally with or without remainder • Regrouping from values of a higher place (tens) to a lower place (ones) in division
Division with regrouping in hundreds, tens and ones	• Expressing a number as a sum of values of different places • Dividing equally with or without remainder • Regrouping from values of a higher place (e.g. hundreds) to a lower place (e.g. tens) in division
Assessment Book – Test 3	
8 Solving Word Problems 2: Multiplication and Division	
Multiplication: one-step word problems	• The multiple concept in multiplication is used to compare two sets of items • Bar diagrams can be based on problem situations in multiplication
Multiplication: two-step word problems	• Multiplication concepts including 'multiple' and 'group and item' are used for solving two-step word problems • Addition concepts such as 'adding on' and 'part-whole' are used for solving two-step word problems • Subtraction concepts such as 'taking away' and 'part-whole' are used for solving two-step word problems
Division: one-step word problems	• The division concepts: finding the number of groups and the number of items in each group are applied • Division is the inverse of multiplication
Division: two-step word problems	• Division concepts using 'group and item' are used for solving two-step word problems • Addition concepts such as 'adding on' and 'part-whole' are used for solving two-step word problems • Subtraction concepts such as 'taking away' and 'part-whole' are used for solving two-step word problems
9 Mental Calculations	
Mental addition	• Applying number bonds to assist mental calculations
Mental subtraction	• Applying number bonds in subtraction
More mental addition	• Relating a number that is close to 100 to a number bond and applying the number bond to do mental addition
Mental multiplication	• Reversing the order of groups and items in a multiplication concept produces the same product
Mental division	• Division is the inverse of multiplication
Practice Book – Review 4	
Practice Book – Revision 2	
Assessment Book – Test 4, Challenging Problems 2, Check-up 2	

Unit title	Key concepts
10 Money	
Addition	• Adding money is similar to adding whole numbers
Subtraction	• Subtracting money is similar to subtracting whole numbers
Word problems	• Concepts in adding and subtracting whole numbers are applied in problems involving money
11 Length, Mass and Volume	
Metres and centimetres	• Visualising and measuring in compound units, metres (m) and centimetres (cm)
Kilometres and metres	• Visualising and measuring in compound units, kilometres (km) and metres (m)
Kilograms and grams	• Visualisation and measurement of a kilogram (kg) and a gram (g)
Litres and millilitres	• Visualisation and measurement of volume and capacity in litres (ℓ) and millilitres (ml)
12 Solving Word Problems: Length, Mass and Volume	
One-step word problems	• Concepts of addition, subtraction, multiplication and division in whole numbers are applied to solve word problems on length, mass and volume
Two-step word problems	• Concepts in the four operations are applied to solve two-step word problems
Practice Book – Review 5	
Assessment Book – Test 5	
13 Bar Graphs	
Making bar graphs with scales	• A bar graph represents synthesised data for presentation
Reading and interpreting bar graphs	• Whole number concepts are applied to bar graphs in reading and interpretation of concepts
14 Fractions	
Numerator and denominator	• A whole is divided into parts and the fraction symbol is used to determine the parts of the whole • The terms 'numerator' and 'denominator' give precise definition of parts of a whole
Understanding equivalent fractions	• A length model with bars showing parts of whole is used to represent fractions • Two equal parts of different divisions taken from the same whole number, with the same size, are equivalent
More equivalent fractions: short cut	• The multiplying factor technique is applied to find equivalent fractions • The dividing factor technique is applied to find equivalent fractions

Unit title	Key concepts
Comparing fractions	• Two fractions are equal when they are expressed as equivalent fractions • Two fractions can be compared by referring to the values of the numerators when the denominators of the two fractions are the same • Two fractions can be compared by referring to the values of the denominator when the numerators of the two fractions are the same
Adding fractions	• Two fractions are related when the denominator of one fraction is a multiple of the denominator of the other fraction • When adding related fractions, the related fractions are changed to like fractions first
Subtracting fractions	• Two fractions are related when the denominator of one fraction is a multiple of the denominator of the other fraction • When subtracting related fractions, the related fractions are changed to like fractions first
Practice Book – Review 6	
Practice Book – Revision 3	
Assessment Book – Test 6, Challenging Problems 3, Check-up 3	
15 Time	
Telling the time	• Using 'past' and 'to' in telling the time
Conversion of hours and minutes	• Pupils use 1 h = 60 mins to convert the time
Addition	• Hours and minutes can be added like whole numbers • Regrouping concepts (60 mins = 1 h) are applied to whole numbers
Subtraction	• Hours and minutes can be subtracted like whole numbers • Regrouping concepts (60 mins = 1 h) are applied to whole numbers
Duration in hours and minutes	• Say the duration of time in hours, minutes and hours and minutes
Word problems	• Use of the unitary method is required to solve problems
16 Angles	
Understanding angles	• An angle is a measure of the amount of turning
Identifying angles	• Angles are measurements of turning which can also be made using 2D shapes
Right angles	• A right angle is a special type of angle, which is formed by two straight lines meeting at a point

Unit title	Key concepts
Assessment Book – Test 7	
17 Perpendicular and Parallel Lines	
Perpendicular lines	• When two straight lines intersect each other at right angles, they are perpendicular to each other
Drawing perpendicular lines	• Perpendicular lines are made when two lines meet at a right angle
Parallel lines	• Parallel lines are two straight lines drawn in such a way that they will never meet and the distance between them will always be the same
Drawing parallel lines	
18 Area and Perimeter	
Area	• Area is the amount of space that covers the surface of a shape • The amount of space is measured by the number of standard units
Square centimetres (cm²)	• A square centimetre is a standard unit for measuring area
Square metres (m²)	• A square metre is a standard unit for measuring bigger areas
Perimeter and area	• Perimeter is the distance around a shape • Area is the amount of surface that covers the surface of the shape
More perimeter	• Perimeter is the distance around a shape
Area of a rectangle	• The area of a rectangle is the amount of space that covers the surface • The area of a rectangle is the same as length × width of the rectangle
Practice Book – Review 7	
Practice Book – Revision 4	
Assessment Book – Test 8, Challenging Problems 4, Check-up 4	

Unit I: Numbers to 10 000

Medium-term plan

Week	Learning Objectives	Thinking Skills	Resources
I	**(I) Counting** Pupils will be able to: • count in ones, tens, hundreds and thousands, and read and write their corresponding numbers and number words • recognise concrete representations of numbers to 10 000 • recognise that 10 hundreds = 1 thousand • translate numbers from (i) models to words and figures (ii) figures to words (iii) words to figures • recognise and interpret sentences associated with tens and ones	• Comparing • Classifying • Sequencing • Identifying relationships	• Pupil Textbook 3A, pp 6 to 10 • Practice Book 3A, pp 5 to 8 • Teacher's Guide 3A, pp 6 to 10

Unit 1: Numbers to 10 000

Medium-term plan

Week	Learning Objectives	Thinking Skills	Resources
1	**(2) Place value** Pupils will be able to: • represent numbers as thousands, hundreds, tens and ones in a place value chart • use a place value chart to show concrete representations of thousands, hundreds, tens and ones given a number to 10 000 • read and write numerals in a place value chart given a set of concrete representations and vice versa • state the place and value of each digit in a number • write a 4-digit number in terms of thousands, hundreds, tens and ones • write a 4-digit number as the sum of the values of each digit in the number	• Comparing • Classifying • Sequencing • Identifying relationships	• Pupil Textbook 3A, pp 11 to 15 • Practice Book 3A, pp 9 to 12 • Teacher's Guide 3A, pp 11 to 15

Unit I: Numbers to 10 000

Medium-term plan

Week	Learning Objectives	Thinking Skills	Resources
1–2	**(3) Comparing, order and pattern** Pupils will be able to: • use the 'comparing thousands, hundreds, tens and ones' strategy to compare numbers to 10 000 • compare numbers to find 'greater/smaller than' and the 'greatest/smallest' • identify the number which is 1/10/100/1000 more/less than a number • compare numbers and arrange them in ascending or descending order • compare numbers by place value to look for a pattern to complete the number series	• Comparing • Identifying relationships	• Pupil Textbook 3A, pp 16 to 23 • Practice Book 3A, pp 13 to 18 • Teacher's Guide 3A, pp 16 to 23

Unit I: Numbers to 10 000

Medium-term plan

Week	Learning Objectives	Thinking Skills	Resources
1–2	*Let's Explore!* This task enables pupils to make use of place and value to make different 4-digit numbers and to identify the smallest and greatest number in each set of numbers they have made. *Maths Journal* Pupils will be able to: • express their understanding of the process of comparing and ordering numbers • express their understanding of place and value by listing the similarities and differences between pairs of numbers		
2	*Put On Your Thinking Caps!* Pupils will be able to apply number and place value concepts to find the missing digits in a number.	• Comparing • Logical reasoning	• Pupil Textbook 3A, p 24 • Practice Book 3A, pp 19 to 22 • Teacher's Guide 3A, p 24

Numbers to 10 000

Learning objectives: Counting

Pupils will be able to:

- count in ones, tens, hundreds and thousands, and read and write their corresponding numbers and number words
- recognise concrete representations of numbers to 10 000
- recognise that 10 hundreds = 1 thousand
- translate numbers from
  (i) models to words and figures
  (ii) figures to words
  (iii) words to figures
- recognise and interpret sentences associated with tens and ones

Key concept

Counting numbers up to 10 000 by using concrete representations and strategies of ones, tens, hundreds and thousands

What you will need

- Base ten equipment

Teaching sequence

- Counting numbers up to 1000 by using concrete representations and strategies of 1s, 10s and 100s.

- Revise by showing concrete representations of 10 cubes making 1 rod; 10 rods making 1 hundred.
- Make a concrete representation of 1 thousand using 10 flats of 100 cubes each.
- Then introduce 10 hundreds = 1000.
- Revise counting in tens up to 100 using the rods. Then count in hundreds up to 1000 using the 100-flats. Ask pupils to count in hundreds: 100, 200, 300, 400, 500, 600, 700, 800, 900, 1000.
- Show pupils how to write the number '1000'.
- Show pupils that 1 block represents 1000 or one thousand.

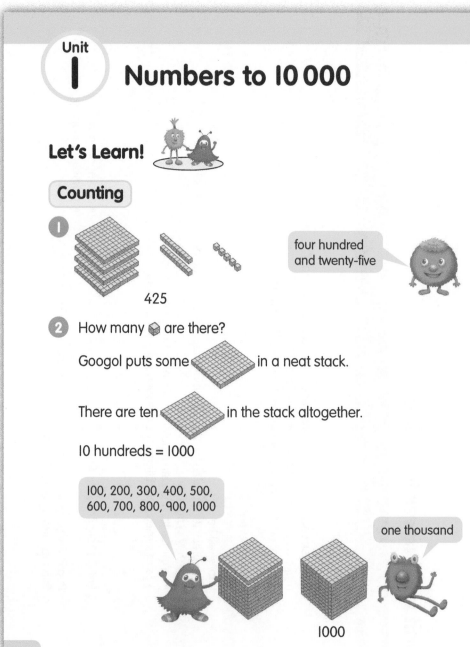

Additional activity

- Draw a place value chart on the board.
- Ask pupils to place I one in the correct position in the place value chart.
- Do the same for I ten, I hundred and I thousand.
- Ask pupils to read the number they have made (IIII). Write this in words (one thousand one hundred and eleven).

- Give pupils a 4-digit number, e.g., I005, 2037, 4327, 5I00.
- Ask pupils to write the correct numbers and words and fill in the correct numerals in the place value chart.

Thinking skills

- Comparing
- Classifying
- Sequencing
- Identifying relationships

Numbers to 10 000 **Unit I**

3 How many 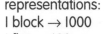 are there?

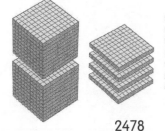

2478

two thousand, four hundred and seventy-eight

4 How many are there?
four thousand and seventy-nine

Write in words.

Write in numbers. 4079

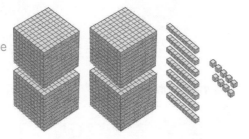

5 Write in words.

a 6257 six thousand, two hundred and fifty-seven

b 8540 eight thousand, five hundred and forty

c 7601 seven thousand, six hundred and one

d 3094 three thousand and ninety-four

6 Write in numbers.

a eight thousand, six hundred and twenty-nine 8629

b four thousand, seven hundred and thirty 4730

c five thousand and eighty-four 5084

d seven thousand and ten 7010

Home Maths — Help your child to write in numbers by doing this:
six thousand   two hundred and five
6000 + 200 + 5 = 6205

7

Teaching sequence

3

- Summarise these concrete representations:
  I block → 1000
  I flat → 100
  I rod → 10
  I cube → I
- Demonstrate how to count up to 2478, using concrete representations of the numbers. As you count and add, say:
  1000, 2000, 2400, 2470, 2478

4

- Ask pupils to count using concrete representations.
- Ask them to write the numeral.
- Then ask them to write the numbers in words.

5

- Pupils should read the numbers and write them in words. Show the first one as an example. Read the numeral: 6257. Then write in words: six thousand two hundred and fifty-seven. Show pupils the strategy for reading and writing numbers.

6

- Ask pupils to read the numbers and write them in numerals.

Teaching sequence

- Using blocks, demonstrate and explain how to get to 10 000 from 9000 by counting hundreds, tens and ones:
9000, 9100, 9200, ...
... 9900, 9910, 9920, 9930, ...
... 9990, 9991, 9992, ...
... 9998, 9999, 10 000

8

- Count on in ones. Relate the strategy for counting (from **7**) to show how to count in ones from 4326 to 4327.

  Explain that to get the next number, you count on in ones. You can ask this question: "What is 1 more than 4326?"

  Then show the next number.

- Pupils should count on in ones to complete the sequence of numbers. They should see a pattern.

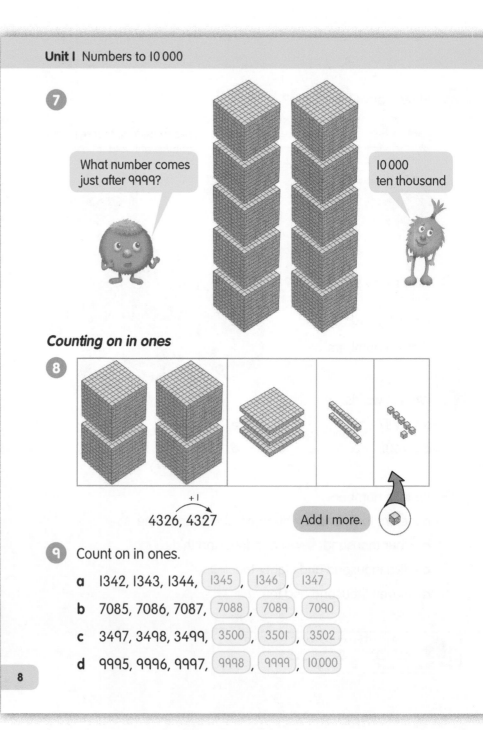

Counting on in tens

⑩

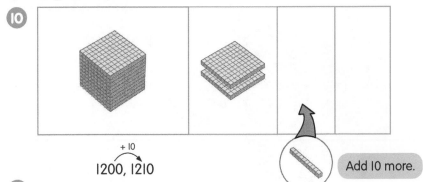

+ 10
1200, 1210

Add 10 more.

⑪ Count on in tens.

a   3840, 3850, 3860, (3870), (3880), (3890)

b   6161, 6171, 6181, (6191), (6201), (6211)

Counting on in hundreds

⑫

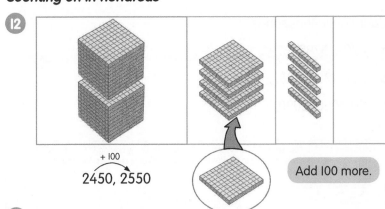

+ 100
2450, 2550

Add 100 more.

⑬ Count on in hundreds.

a   5345, 5445, 5545, (5645), (5745), (5845)

b   8670, 8770, 8870, (8970), (9070), (9170)

9

Additional activity

- Ask pupils to write a number.
- Ask them to count on in hundreds to get the next five numbers.

Teaching sequence

⑩

- Relate the strategy for counting (from **7**) to show how to count on in tens from 1200 to 1210.
- Show pupils how to use base ten equipment to make the number 1200. Ask them: "*What is 10 more than 1200?*" and ask them to add a 10-rod. Encourage them to give the answer.

⑪

- Ask pupils to count on in tens to complete the sequence of numbers. Encourage them to look for a pattern.

⑫

- Show pupils how to use base ten equipment to make the number 2450. Ask them: "*What is 100 more than 2450?*" Add a 100-flat. Encourage them to give the answer.

⑬

- Pupils should count on in hundreds to complete the sequence of numbers. Encourage them to look for a pattern.

Additional activities

1. Ask pupils to write a number. Then count on in thousands to get the next five numbers.

2. Ask pupils to work in groups and give each group some base ten equipment. Ask each group to make a number with the base ten equipment, for example: 3578. Ask them to add ones (one at a time until they have added 5 ones), and to write down the numbers: 3578, 3579, 3580, 3581, 3582.

Pupils need to change the ones to a ten when the ones place contains ten cubes. Similarly, add 10-rods, 100-flats and 1000-blocks (for the 1000-blocks, make sure the number shown does not go beyond 10 000).

3. Ask pupils to write five 4-digit numbers. Pupils should find 'I more than', 'I less than', '10 more than', '10 less than', '100 more than', '100 less than', '1000 more than' and '1000 less than' that number.

Independent work

Practice I in Practice Book 3A, pp 5 to 8.

Teaching sequence

- Show pupils how to use base ten equipment to make the number 6206. Ask them: "What is 1000 more than 6206?" and add a big cube. Ask them for the answer, which is 7206.

- Ask pupils to count on in thousands to complete the sequence of numbers. Encourage them to look for a pattern.

Counting on in thousands

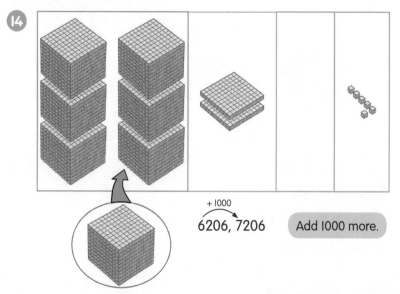

+ 1000

6206, 7206   Add 1000 more.

(15) Count on in thousands.

a   4792, 5792, 6792, (7792), (8792), (9792)

b   287, 1287, 2287, (3287), (4287), (5287)

c   90, 1090, 2090, (3090), (4090), (5090)

Home Maths

Help your child to see which digit changes when you count on by adding I, 10, 100 or 1000. For example, when we count on in hundreds, the hundreds digit changes. We add 100 to get the next number:

4**5**35, 4**6**35, 4**7**35, ...,
+ 100   + 100

In some cases, other digits can change too. For example, when we add 100 to 4**9**35, we get **50**35. Here both the hundreds and thousands digits change.

Practice Book 3A, p.5

10

Learning objectives: Place value

Pupils will be able to:

- represent numbers as thousands, hundreds, tens and ones in a place value chart
- use a place value chart to show concrete representations of thousands, hundreds, tens and ones given a number to 10 000
- read and write numerals in a place value chart given a set of concrete representations and vice versa
- state the place and value of each digit in a number
- write a 4-digit number in terms of thousands, hundreds, tens and ones
- write a 4-digit number as the sum of the values of each digit in the number

Key concept

The digits of a number have their own values in terms of ones, tens, hundreds and thousands.

Thinking skills

- Comparing
- Classifying
- Sequencing
- Identifying relationships

What you will need

- Base ten equipment
- Place value charts

Numbers to 10 000 **Unit 1**

Let's Learn!

Place value

1 How many are there?

Thousands	Hundreds	Tens	Ones
2	4	7	5

| stands for 2 thousands or 2000 | stands for 4 hundreds or 400 | stands for 7 tens or 70 | stands for 5 ones or 5 |

2475 = 2 thousands 4 hundreds 7 tens 5 ones

In 2475:
the digit 4 is in the hundreds place
the digit 7 stands for 70
the value of the digit 5 is 5.

2475 = 2000 + 400 + 70 + 5

In 2475:
the digit 2 is in the thousands place
the digit 2 stands for 2000
the value of the digit 2 is 2000.

11

Teaching sequence

1

- At this stage, pupils are able to interpret and read numbers represented by concrete representations. Show the class 2475 using base ten equipment and write the numeral in a place value chart. Highlight the place value headings for ones, tens, hundreds and thousands.

- Explain the different ways of presenting the place value of the digits of the number, as shown in the textbook. For example, the digit 2 stands for 2 thousands or 2000.

- Show and explain the various ways to present the number 2475:

  Reading and writing:
  2 thousands 4 hundreds 7 tens 5 ones

  Values of each digit:
  The digit 4 is in the hundreds place, 7 stands for 70 and so on.

  Writing as a sum:
  2475 = 2000 + 400 + 70 + 5

Teaching sequence

- Following the earlier explanation, ask pupils to work on this exercise.
- Ask them to interpret the base ten equipment and find the values of each digit in the place value chart.
- Then ask pupils to interpret the numeral 1329 and write the value of each digit in its place.
- Next ask them to find the missing numbers, which will illustrate their understanding of place value.

- Ask pupils to work on this exercise as reinforcement of the concepts they have just learnt.

2 How many ⬛ are there?

Thousands	Hundreds	Tens	Ones
1	3	2	9

a 1329 = (1) thousand (3) hundreds (2) tens (9) ones

b 1329 = (1000) + (300) + (20) + (9)

c In 1329,

the digit (1) is in the thousands place.

It stands for (1000).

Its value is (1000).

3 a In 2548,
the digit (5) is in the hundreds place.

The digit 4 stands for (40).

The value of the digit 8 is (8).

b In 2562, the values of the digit 2 are:

2 5 6 2

(2000) ←⎯⎯ ⎯⎯→ (2)

12

Additional activities

- Ask pupils to work in groups. Ask one pupil to roll a 10-sided dice four times and to write down the digits they get. The other group members should make as many 4-digit numbers as possible. Check how many different 4-digit numbers can be made.
- Ask a pupil from each group to show a 4-digit number using base ten equipment. Ask the other group members to each write three sentences about the number and then to check each other's answers.

What you will need

- 10-sided dice
- Base ten equipment
- Worksheet (see Photocopy master 1 on page 261)

Game

4 **Roll and show!**

How to play:

Players: 2 to 4
You will need:
- a 10-sided dice
- base ten equipment
- a place value worksheet

1 Work in two groups, the Rollies and the Showies.

2 The Rollies roll the dice four times to get four numbers.

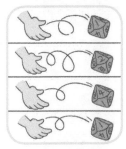

3 The Showies then use the numbers to make a 4-digit number. They write the number and show the number using base ten equipment.

4 The Rollies check the answer. Each group takes turns to roll and show! Play at least five rounds.

The group with the most correct answers wins!

13

Teaching sequence

4 *Game*

- Follow the steps in the textbook and ask pupils to roll and show the 4-digit numbers.

Teaching sequence

- Use base ten equipment to show pupils the number 4827 and ask what each of its digits stands for. Show them that adding the values of 4000, 800, 20 and 7 make 4827 or

$$
\begin{array}{r}
4000 \\
800 \\
20 \\
+ \quad 7 \\
\hline
4827 \\
\end{array}
$$

or

$$4000 + 800 + 20 + 7 = 4827$$

- Ask pupils to complete this exercise to help them master the place value concept.

I have 4827.

Thousands	Hundreds	Tens	Ones

4000, 800, 20 and 7 make 4827.

$4000 + 800 + 20 + 7 = 4827$

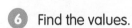

6 Find the values.

a   5000, 300, 10 and 6 make 5316 .

b   7000, 200, 80 and 9 make 7289 .

c   3000 + 100 + 70 + 5 = 3175

14

Independent work

Practice 2 in Practice Book 3A,
pp 9 to 12.

7 Answer these questions.

a What is the value of each digit?

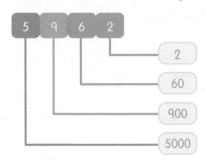

b In 6925,

the digit ⬡ 6 is in the thousands place.

The digit 9 stands for ⬡ 900 .

The value of the digit 2 is ⬡ 20 .

c Find the values.

⬡ 4000 , 300, 60 and I make 4361.

6720 is 6000, 700 and ⬡ 20 .

5000, ⬡ 800 and 5 is 5805.

7000, 400 and 8 make ⬡ 7408 .

d Find the missing numbers.

3000 + 900 + 10 + 5 = ⬡ 3915

1324 = ⬡ 1000 + 300 + 20 + 4

7610 = 7000 + ⬡ 600 + 10

4000 + 50 = ⬡ 4050

8 + 500 + 9000 = ⬡ 9508

Practice Book 3A, p.9 ▷ 15

Teaching sequence

- Ask pupils to complete these exercises to help them master the place value concept.

Learning objectives: Comparing, order and pattern

Pupils will be able to:

- use the 'comparing thousands, hundreds, tens and ones' strategy to compare numbers to 10 000
- compare numbers to find 'greater/smaller than' and the 'greatest/smallest'
- identify the number that is 1/10/100/1000 more/less than a number
- compare numbers and arrange them in ascending or descending order
- compare numbers by place value to look for a pattern to complete the number series

Key concept

Numbers up to 10 000 can be compared and arranged in ascending or descending order.

Teaching sequence

- Use base ten equipment to provide pupils with a concrete representation of the two numbers: 6051 and 4987.
- Ask pupils to compare the digits in the thousands place, by referring to the concrete representations, to find the greater number.
- Pupils should see that 6 thousands is greater than 4 thousands.

  Pupils should see and infer that 6051 is greater than 4987.

- **Note**: Comparing of numbers must start with the greatest place value – thousands place first, then hundreds, tens and ones.

Unit 1 Numbers to 10 000

Let's Learn!

Comparing, order and pattern

1. Jack wants to choose the greater number. Which set will Jack choose, Set A or Set B?

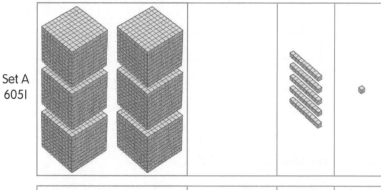

Set A
6051

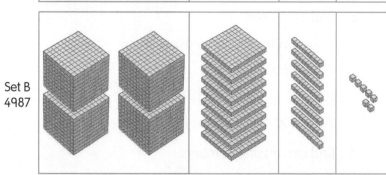

Set B
4987

Compare the thousands.

6 thousands is greater than 4 thousands.

6051 is greater than 4987.

Jack will choose Set A.

16

Thinking skills

- Comparing
- Identifying relationships

2 If the two numbers have the same number of thousands, we compare the hundreds instead.

Now Jack wants to choose the smaller number.

Which set will Jack choose, Set A or Set B?

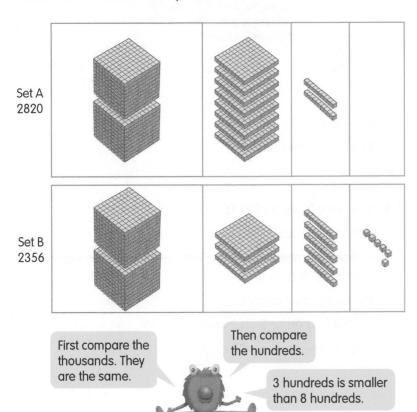

Set A
2820

Set B
2356

First compare the thousands. They are the same.

Then compare the hundreds.

3 hundreds is smaller than 8 hundreds.

2356 is smaller than 2820.

Jack will choose Set B.

17

Teaching sequence

2

- Using the pictures in the textbook, show pupils that the digits in the thousands place are the same.
- Show them that 8 hundreds is greater than 3 hundreds.
- Pupils should infer that the number in Set A is greater than the number in Set B.

Additional activity

Ask pupils to work in pairs. Ask Pupil A to write a 4-digit number. Pupil B should then write a 4-digit number that is greater than Pupil A's number by changing one digit of their number. Pupil A should then write another greater number by changing one digit of Pupil B's number. Pupils should continue to take turns to do this until no greater 4-digit number can be made.

Teaching sequence

- Guide pupils to compare the numbers in the thousands, hundreds, tens and ones places.
- They should see that the thousands and hundreds are the same and infer that 6870 is greater than 6829.
- Introduce the following strategy to help pupils compare numbers: Place the two numbers on top of each other. For example:

  6870
  6829

  In this way, pupils should see that the thousands and the hundreds are the same. In the tens column, 7 is greater than 2, so the number on the top is greater than the number below.

- Guide pupils to see that the thousands, hundreds, and tens are the same using the strategy given in ③.
- Encourage them to infer that 2748 is greater than 2745.

---

③ You have 6829 and 6870.

Which is greater?

Which is smaller?

If the two numbers have the same number of thousands and hundreds, we compare the tens instead.

2 tens is smaller than 7 tens.

6870 is greater than 6829.

6829 is smaller than 6870.

④ You have 2748 and 2745.

Which is greater?

The two numbers have the same number of thousands, hundreds and tens.

We compare the ones.

8 ones is greater than 5 ones.

2748 is greater than 2745.

18

Additional activities

1. As a whole-class activity, compare numbers with:

   a) different thousands (e.g., 5764, 3409 and 1287).

   b) equal thousands but different hundreds (e.g., 7239, 7386 and 7670).

   c) equal thousands and hundreds but different tens (e.g., 2372, 2345 and 2389).

   d) equal thousands, hundreds and tens but different ones (e.g., 9780, 9788 and 9787).

2. If you have time, split the class into small groups. Give each group a set of 4-digit numbers and ask them to arrange the numbers in ascending or descending order. Encourage the groups to check they have the correct answers.

---

5 Which is greater? Which is smaller? Use **greater than** or **smaller than**.

a

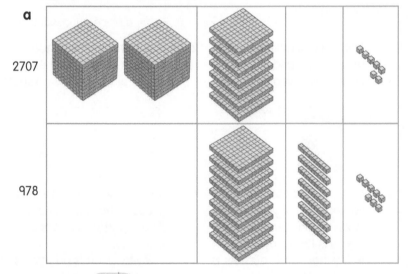

2707

978

2707 is greater than 978.

b 4058 is smaller than 4610.

c 3135 is smaller than 3181.

d 6289 is greater than 6280.

 Compare the thousands, hundreds, tens and ones.

6 Compare 4769, 4802 and 4738.

Which is the smallest?   4738

Which is the greatest?   4802

7 a Arrange the numbers in order, beginning with the smallest.

| 2389 | 3001 | 999 | 3010 | 999, 2389, 3001, 3010 |

b Arrange the numbers in order, beginning with the greatest.

| 4790 | 974 | 7049 | 9107 | 9107, 7049, 4790, 974 |

19

Teaching sequence

5 and **6**

- Encourage pupils to practise the strategy by working on these exercises.

- Ask them to place the numbers on top of each other and align the places of the numbers accordingly.

7

- Pupils should arrange the numbers in ascending or descending order.

- Ask pupils to align the numbers as shown. Ensure that the places of each number are aligned in the same column.

      2389
      3001
       999
      3010

- Compare the thousands: 3001 and 3010 have the greatest thousands of all the numbers shown.
3010 is greater than 3001.
2389 comes third and 999 has the smallest value.

What you will need

Worksheet (see Photocopy master 2 on page 262)

Additional activity

Draw the number 9999 on the board. Ask pupils to work in pairs. Ask Pupil A to write a 4-digit number that is smaller than 9999 by changing one digit of the number. Ask Pupil B to repeat the exercise using Pupil A's number. Pupils should continue to take turns until no smaller number can be made.

Teaching sequence

- Ask pupils to carry out the activity shown to guess a number.

Activity

8 Work in pairs.

Players: 2
You will need:
- a place value worksheet

1 Think of a 4-digit number using 1, 2, 3 and 4. Use each digit only once.

2314

2 Your partner tries to guess your number. They write their guess on the place value worksheet.

Thousands	Hundreds	Tens	Ones
1	2	4	3

3 Give your partner clues. For example, if your number is 2314, and your partner's guess is 1243, say:
- My thousands number is greater than yours.
- My hundreds number is greater than yours.
- My tens number is smaller than yours.
- My ones number is greater than yours.

4 Your partner writes another guess in the second row. If your partner's guess is 2134, say:
- My thousands number is the same as yours.
- My hundreds number is greater than yours.
- My tens number is smaller than yours.
- My ones number is the same as yours.

Thousands	Hundreds	Tens	Ones
1	2	4	3
2	1	3	4

5 Your partner circles the numbers that they guess correctly and keeps guessing until they get the whole number. Swap roles!

Thousands	Hundreds	Tens	Ones
1	2	4	3
(2)	1	3	(4)

20

Additional activity

Pupil A writes a sequence of 10 numbers. They then rub out two of the numbers. Pupil B finds the unknown values.

Pupils A and B swap roles.

9 This is a number track.

Some numbers on the track are missing.

Find the numbers.

To find the missing number, the rule is to subtract 10 from the number after it.

− 10

1497 1507

10 less than 1507 is 1497.		10 more than 1527 is 1537.

1427	1437	1447	1457	?	1477	1487	?	1507	1517	1527	?	1547

10 more than 1457 is 1467.

To find the missing number, the rule is to add 10 to the number before it.

+ 10

1457 1467

10 The numbers on this number track are arranged in a pattern. Find the missing numbers.

100 more than 5583 is 5683 .		100 more than 6083 is 6183 .

5283	5383	5483	5583	?	5783	5883	?	6083	?	6283	6383	6483

100 less than 6083 is 5983 .

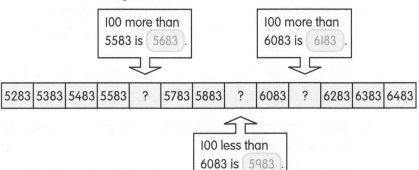

21

Teaching sequence

9

- Demonstrate to pupils how to check whether a sequence of numbers is arranged in a pattern. They should check a few to ensure that the pattern is correct.

  For example, 1437 is 10 more than 1427 and so on. Then they can apply the pattern to find the unknown values.

10

- Using the procedure given in **9** , guide pupils to find the unknown values.

Objective of activity

This task enables pupils to make use of place and value to make different 4-digit numbers and to identify the smallest and greatest number in each set of numbers they have made.

Independent work

Practice 3 in Practice Book 3A, pp 13 to 18.

Teaching sequence

- Demonstrate the method for finding the answers to these problems.

Step 1: Write the number 5893.
Step 2: Show 5893 + 10.
Step 3: Add to find the answer.

$$+ 10$$
$$5893 \rightarrow 5903$$

Work through another example using 'less than'.

$$- 10$$
$$4203 \rightarrow 4193$$

- Guide pupils to apply the 'more than' and 'less than' strategy to determine the pattern. Ask pupils to work on the questions.

13 *Let's Explore!*

- Pupils should write 4-digit numbers following the instructions in the textbook.

11 Find the values.

   a 10 more than 5893 is 5903 .

   b 10 less than 4203 is 4193 .

   c 100 more than 3967 is 4067 .

   d 100 less than 7062 is 6962 .

12 Complete the number patterns.

   a 5843, 5833, 5823 , 5813, 5803 , 5793

   b 6893 , 6903 , 6913, 6923 , 6933, 6943

   c 7662, 7762 , 7862, 7962, 8062 , 8162

   d 4420, 4320, 4220 , 4120, 4020, 3920

   e 7200, 7220, 7240, 7260 , 7280, 7300 , 7320

   f 880, 980, 1080 , 1180 , 1280, 1380, 1480, 1580 , 1680

   g 8472, 8672, 8872 , 9072 , 9272, 9472, 9672

Practice Book 3A, p.13

Let's Explore!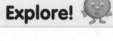

13 a Write the digits 4, 5, 6 and 7 on four different cards. Arrange the four cards to make as many numbers as possible with:

4 in the thousands place 6   6 in the thousands place. 6

How many numbers can you make?

   b Subtract the smallest number from the greatest number in the set of numbers with:

4 in the thousands place 198   6 in the thousands place. 297

22

Objective of activity

Pupils will be able to:

- express their understanding of the process of comparing and ordering numbers.
- express their understanding of place and value by listing the similarities and differences between pairs of numbers.

Additional activity

Ask pupils to work in groups of 4. Provide each group with a sequence of numbers that cannot make a number pattern. Ask pupils to rearrange the digits within the numbers so that a number pattern can be made.

Maths Journal

14 a Peter has three numbers. | 1984   2084   1884 |

He arranges the numbers in order, beginning with the smallest.

| 1884 |, | 1984 |, | 2084 |

Peter uses the steps below.

Step I: I compare the thousands values of the three numbers.

Step 2: I can see that 2084 is the greatest number.

Step 3: I compare the hundreds values of the other two numbers.

Step 4: I can see that 1884 is the smallest number.

b Ella has three numbers. | 9049   9654   8785 |

Arrange the numbers in order, beginning with the greatest.

| 9654 |, | 9049 |, | 8785 |

Write down the steps to help Ella find the answer.

Step I: ( ) Compare the thousands values of the three numbers.

Step 2: ( ) See that 8785 is the smallest number.

Step 3: ( ) Compare the hundreds values of the other two numbers.

Step 4: ( ) See that 9654 is the greatest number.

23

Teaching sequence

14 *Maths Journal*

- Work through the steps for comparing and arranging a set of numbers in ascending order. Ask pupils to write the steps for arranging another set of numbers in descending order.

Objective of activity

Pupils will be able to apply number and place value concepts to find the missing digits in a number.

Thinking skills

- Comparing
- Logical reasoning

Independent work

Challenging Practice, Problem Solving and *Maths Journal* in Practice Book 3A, pp 19 to 22.

Additional activity

Ask pupils to work in pairs to play a number guessing game, using the place value concept.

Pupil A writes down two 4-digit numbers and then rubs out one digit from each number.

Pupil A gives clues, relating to place value, to Pupil B.

Pupil B guesses the missing numbers using the clues.

Pupils A and B swap roles.

Teaching sequence

15 *Put On Your Thinking Caps!*

- Ask pupils to use the clues to find the unknown digits for the three numbers.

Put On Your Thinking Caps!

15 Ruby wrote three 4-digit numbers on a piece of paper.
She accidentally spilt some paint on the paper.
Some digits were covered by the paint.
Using the clues, help Ruby to find the digits covered by the paint.

```
4  7  5
2  1
3  3     0
```

CLUES

The sum of all the ones digits is 17.

The ones digit of the first number is the greatest 1-digit number.

The digit in the tens place of the second number is one more than the digit in the tens place of the first number.

The tens digit of the third number is 4 less than the tens digit of the second number.

$9 + 8 = 17$
The ones digit of the first number is 9.
The ones digit of the second number is 8.
$5 + 1 = 6$
The tens digit of the second number is 6.
$6 - 4 = 2$
The tens digit of the third number is 2.
The three numbers are 4759, 2168 and 3320.

Practice Book 3A, p.19   Practice Book 3A, p.20

24

Date: _____

Unit 1 Numbers to 10 000

Practice 1   Counting

 How many are there?

a				2651
b				6550
c				9204
d				1009

2 Write the numbers in words.

a 2830

two thousand, eight hundred and thirty

b 7118

seven thousand, one hundred and eighteen

c 1805

one thousand, eight hundred and five

d 3009

three thousand and nine

e 4040

four thousand and forty

3 Which animals ate the carrots?
Fill in the boxes with the correct numbers and match them with the letters to find out!

a nine thousand | 9000 | **h**

b five thousand and nine | 5009 | **a**

c five thousand and sixty-eight | 5068 | **e**

d three thousand, two hundred and sixty | 3260 | **s**

e three thousand, two hundred and six | 3206 | **t**

f six thousand, eight hundred and thirty-five | 6835 | **r**

g two thousand and seventy | 2070 | **s**

h one thousand, four hundred | 1400 | **o**

Now match the letters to the numbers.

The | h | o | r | s | e | s | ate the carrots.
| 9000 | 1400 | 6835 | 2070 | 5068 | 3260 |

Date: _____

Practice 2　Place value

1. Fill in the spaces.

a　2

2 thousands	6 hundreds	3 tens	9 ones
or 2000	or 600	or 30	or 9

b　3

3 thousands	0 hundreds	9 tens	2 ones
or 3000	or 0	or 90	or 2

c　6

6 thousands	5 hundreds	0 tens	0 ones
or 6000	or 500	or 0	or 0

---

4. Count in ones, tens, hundreds or thousands.

a　2065, 2066, _2067_, 2068, _2069_, _____, 2070

b　6418, 6417, _6416_, _____, 6415, 6414, _____, _6413_

c　_7523_, 7533, _____, 7543, 7553, 7563, _____, _7573_

d　1674, _____, _1664_, 1654, _____, _1644_, 1634, 1624

e　3307, 3407, 3507, _____, _3607_, 3707, _____, _3807_

f　_8526_, 8426, _____, 8326, _____, 8226, 8126, 8026

g　3654, 4654, _____, _5654_, 6654, _____, 7654, 8654

h　7062, 6062, _____, _5062_, 4062, _____, 3062, 2062

5. Count in tens.
Colour the stones the frog jumps on.

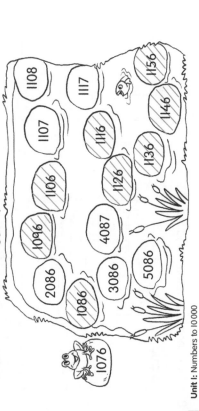

Answers Unit I: Numbers to 10 000　　**27**

2 What does each digit stand for?

Example

6 3 2 1 →
- 1
- 20
- 300
- 6000

b 6 0 5 5 →
- 5
- 50
- 0
- 6000

a 3 4 6 7 →
- 7
- 60
- 400
- 3000

c 1 4 2 0 →
- 0
- 20
- 400
- 1000

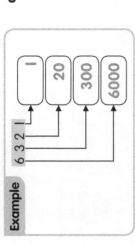

3 Fill in the spaces.

Thousands	Hundreds	Tens	Ones
2	5	4	8

a In 2548, the digit 4 is in the ___tens___ place.
The value of the digit is ___40___.

b In 2548, the digit ___8___ is in the ones place.
The value of the digit is ___8___.

c In 2548, the value of the digit 2 is ___2000___.
It is in the ___thousands___ place.

d In 2548, the value of the digit ___5___ is 500.
It is in the ___hundreds___ place.

4 Find the values.

Example

Thousands	Hundreds	Tens	Ones
(blocks)	(blocks)	(rods)	(dot)

6000 + 600 + 40 + 1 = ___6641___
6000, 600, 40 and 1 make ___6641___.

a

Thousands	Hundreds	Tens	Ones
(blocks)		(rods)	(dots)

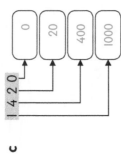

2000 + 30 + 4 = ___2034___
2000, 30 and 4 make ___2034___.

b

Thousands	Hundreds	Tens	Ones
(blocks)		(rod)	

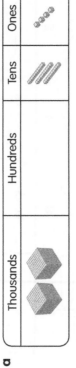

3000 + 20 = ___3020___
3000 and 20 make ___3020___.

Practice 3 Comparing, order and pattern

1 Fill in the spaces.

a

Set A

Thousands	Hundreds	Tens	Ones
7	5	3	2

Set B

Thousands	Hundreds	Tens	Ones
7	3	9	2

Which number is greater? _7532_

The number in Set __A__ is greater than the number

in Set __B__ .

b

Set A

Thousands	Hundreds	Tens	Ones
4	5	6	1

Set B

Thousands	Hundreds	Tens	Ones
4	5	2	3

Which number is smaller? _4523_

The number in Set __B__ is smaller than the number

in Set __A__ .

5 Fill in the boxes.

a 7456 = 7000 + 400 + 50 + 6

b 6391 = 6000 + 300 + 90 + 1

c 6193 = 6000 + 100 + 90 + 3

d 6107 = 6000 + 100 + 7

e 8904 = 8000 + 900 + 4

f 5068 = 5000 + 60 + 8

2 Which is greater? Which is smaller?
Use **greater than** or **smaller than**.

a 3160 is [smaller than] 8620.

b 4500 is [smaller than] 4536.

c 999 is [smaller than] 1000.

d 2391 is [greater than] 2099.

3 Circle the greater number.

a 8687 (8987)

b (1251) 1231

4 Circle the smaller number.

a 2012 (200)

b (7400) 7402

5 Underline the smallest number and circle the greatest number.

6963   6639   6696   (6993)

6 Arrange the numbers in order, beginning with the smallest.

a 2340, 989, 4001

989, 2340, 4001

b 2456, 1456, 6456

1456, 2456, 6456

c 6359, 6059, 6759

6059, 6359, 6759

d 3052, 3057, 3050

3050, 3052, 3057

7 Arrange the numbers in order, beginning with the greatest.

a 5317   5137   5731   5713

5731   5713   5317   5137

b 3761   3671   3617   3716

3761   3716   3671   3617

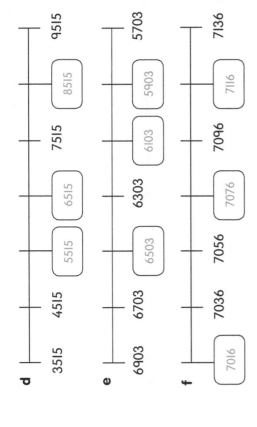

d 3515 4515 5515 6515 7515 8515 9515

e 6903 6703 6503 6303 6103 5903 5703

f 7016 7036 7056 7076 7096 7116 7136

IO Complete the number patterns.

a 5725, 5735, 5745, 5755, 5765, 5775

b 8625, 8725, 8825, 8925, 9025, 9125

c 862, 962, 1062, 1162, 1262, 1362

d 6315, 6215, 6115, 6015, 5915, 5815

---

8 Fill in the spaces.

> **Example**
> I more than 6348 is __6349__.

a 1000 more than 3217 is __4217__.

b 100 less than 5608 is __5508__.

c 10 less than 2000 is __1990__.

q Fill in the missing numbers.

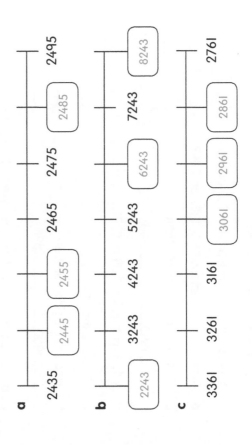

a 2435 2445 2455 2465 2475 2485 2495

b 2243 3243 4243 5243 6243 7243 8243

c 3361 3261 3161 3061 2961 2861 2761

Challenging Practice

1 Look at the numbers. What is the next number?

a

Thousands	Hundreds	Tens	Ones
5	6	2	3
6	6	2	2
7	6	2	1
8	6	2	0

b 5621, 5741, 5861, __5981__

c 6871, 5861, __4851__, 3841

2 Look at the two numbers.

[3551] and [3451]

a Which is smaller? __3451__

b What is the difference between the two numbers? __100__

II Peter and his dad are looking for the library.
Help them follow the correct numbers on the map.

Write your answers in the boxes.

a Which is the smallest: 3456, 8265 or 4456?   [3456]

b Which is the greatest: 1978, 1987 or 1889?   [1987]

c Complete the number pattern.
1980, 1990, _____, 2010   [2000]

d Which is smaller: 8219 or 8291?   [8219]

e 100 more than 1912 is _____.   [2012]

f Find the missing number.
1901, 1900, _____, 1898   [1899]

Colour the path Peter and his dad take to the library.
Which building do they go to?

Building [A]

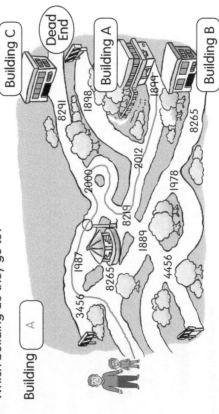

Maths Journal

1 Look at the numbers below.

[6128] [6228]

a Write two sentences showing how they are similar.

Example
> Both have the digit 6 in the thousands place.

Both have the digit 2 in the ___tens___ place.

Both have the digit ___8___ in the ones place.

b Write a sentence showing how they are different.

Example
> The digits in the hundreds place are different.

6228 ___ is 100 more than 6128.

Problem Solving

1 Use the digits 3, 5 and 2 to make 3-digit numbers.

a How many numbers can you make? 6

352   235   253   325   523   532

b What is the smallest number you can make? ___235___

c What is the greatest number you can make? ___532___

2 Fill in the missing numbers.

1042	1041	1040	1039	1038
1049	1048	1047	1046	1039
1047	1046	1045	1044	1040
				1041
			1048	1042
			1047	1043
			1046	

2 Look at the numbers below.

4816   3814

a Write three sentences showing how they are similar.

Answers vary

b Write two sentences showing how they are different.

Answers vary

Unit I: Numbers to I0 000

Unit 2: Addition of Numbers within 10 000

Week	Learning Objectives	Thinking Skills	Resources
2	**(1) The meaning of sum** Pupils will be able to: • relate the word 'sum' to the addition operation • add within 1000 with or without regrouping	• Identifying relationships	• Pupil Textbook 3A, p 25 • Practice Book 3A, pp 23 to 24 • Teacher's Guide 3A, p 37
2	**(2) Simple addition within 10 000** Pupils will be able to: • add within 10 000 without regrouping • add using concrete representations and place value charts • begin column addition by adding the ones, tens, hundreds and thousands in order • add without using concrete representations and without place value charts	• Identifying relationships	• Pupil Textbook 3A, pp 26 to 27 • Practice Book 3A, pp 25 to 28 • Teacher's Guide 3A, pp 38 to 39
3	**(3) Addition with regrouping in hundreds** Pupils will be able to: • add two 4-digit numbers with regrouping in hundreds using concrete representations • show regrouping of hundreds to thousands and hundreds • carry out column addition by adding the hundreds first, then the thousands with regrouping in the hundreds place • add without place value charts *Let's Explore!* This task enables pupils to find out when regrouping in the hundreds place will occur.	• Applying place value relationships • Identifying relationships	• Pupil Textbook 3A, pp 28 to 31 • Practice Book 3A, pp 29 to 30 • Teacher's Guide 3A, pp 40 to 43

Unit 2: Addition of Numbers within 10 000

Week	Learning Objectives	Thinking Skills	Resources
3	**(4) Addition with regrouping in ones, tens and hundreds** Pupils will be able to: • add two 4-digit numbers with regrouping in ones, tens and hundreds using concrete representations • show regrouping of ones to tens and ones; tens to hundreds and tens; hundreds to thousands and hundreds • carry out column addition with regrouping in the ones, tens and hundreds places • solve addition word problems with regrouping by using concrete representations *Maths Journal* Pupils will be able to: • identify two common mistakes made in the addition of two numbers and to explain the mistakes • express their understanding of regrouping by writing down the steps in the procedure for adding two numbers	• Applying place value relationships • Translating words to symbols • Analysing	• Pupil Textbook 3A, pp 32 to 35 • Practice Book 3A, pp 31 to 34 • Teacher's Guide 3A, pp 44 to 47
4	*Put On Your Thinking Caps!* These questions reinforce and consolidate the process of regrouping hundreds. Review 1	• Comparing • Analysing parts and whole	• Pupil Textbook 3A, p 36 • Practice Book 3A, pp 35 to 38 • Teacher's Guide 3A, p 48 • Practice Book 3A, pp 39 to 42

Summative assessment opportunity

Assessment Book 3, Test 1, pp 1 to 6

Addition of Numbers within 10 000

**Learning objectives:
The meaning of sum**

Pupils will be able to:

- relate the word 'sum' to the addition operation
- add within 1000 with or without regrouping

Key concept

The meaning of 'sum' is to add.

Thinking skill

Identifying relationships

Independent work

Practice 1 in Practice Book 3A, pp 23 to 24.

Unit 2

Addition of Numbers within 10 000

Let's Learn!

| The meaning of sum |

① How can you find the sum of the numbers 31 and 45?

What does 'sum' mean?

To find the sum, we have to add the numbers. This is how we add the two numbers.

```
  3 1
+ 4 5
-----
  7 6
```

31   45

?

The **sum** of 31 and 45 is 76.

② Find the sum of these numbers.

a   35 and 59 94   b   220 and 48 268   c   715 and 160 875

③ Farha has 425 stamps.
Peter has 275 stamps.
Find the sum of the number of stamps they have. 700 stamps

Practice Book 3A, p.23

25

Teaching sequence

①

- Introduce and explain the meaning of the word '**sum**'.
- To find the sum of 31 and 45 means to add the numbers 31 and 45.
  "The sum of 31 and 45 is 76."

② and ③

- Ask pupils to complete the exercise and the word problem involving the word 'sum'.

Learning objectives: Simple addition within 10 000

Pupils will be able to:

- add within 10 000 without regrouping
- add using concrete representations and place value charts
- begin column addition by adding the ones, tens, hundreds and thousands in order
- add without using concrete representations and without place value charts

Teaching sequence

- Demonstrate to pupils by representing 1482 and 7516 with base ten equipment or counters in a place value chart.
- Introduce the strategy and procedures for adding numbers: adding from right to left (first add the ones, then the tens and hundreds and finally the thousands).

Key concept

Addition within 10 000 without regrouping

Thinking skill

Identifying relationships

What you will need

- Base ten equipment or counters
- Place value charts

Unit 2 Addition of Numbers within 10 000

Let's Learn!

Simple addition within 10 000

1. Omar needs to find the sum of 1482 and 7516.
   He represents the numbers using base ten equipment.

   1482 + 7516 = ?

Thousands	Hundreds	Tens	Ones

   He gets 8998.

   First add the ones.

   ```
     1 4 8 2
   + 7 5 1 6
   ---------
           8
   ```

   Next add the tens.

   ```
     1 4 8 2
   + 7 5 1 6
   ---------
         9 8
   ```

   Then add the hundreds.

   ```
     1 4 8 2
   + 7 5 1 6
   ---------
       9 9 8
   ```

   Finally add the thousands.

   ```
     1 4 8 2
   + 7 5 1 6
   ---------
     8 9 9 8
   ```

26

Additional activity

Ask pupils to work in pairs. Give each pair a set of addition sums up to 10 000 that do not use regrouping. Ask pupils to work together in their pairs to find the answers.

Independent work

Practice 2 in Practice Book 3A, pp 25 to 28.

Addition of Numbers within 10 000 **Unit 2**

2 The sum of 2653 and 3302 is (5955).

Thousands	Hundreds	Tens	Ones
2	6	5	3
+ 3	3	0	2
5	9	5	5

3 Add.

a
```
   1 6 9 3
 + 5 2 0 4
```
(6897)

b
```
   4 0 2 5
 +   3 6 4
```
(4389)

c
```
   7 1 4 3
 + 1 6 0 2
```
(8745)

d
```
   2 7 0 0
 + 3 2 9 5
```
(5995)

4 Find the sum of these numbers.

a 436 and 9210 9646

b 2421 and 6308 8729

c 5668 and 3020 8688

Practice Book 3A, p.25

27

Teaching sequence

- Ask pupils to work out the sum using a place value chart.
- In this exercise, pupils are guided by place value charts.

- Ask pupils to complete the exercises without concrete representations or place value charts.

- Relate the word 'sum' to the addition sums in this exercise.
- **Note**: Pupils must place the digits in the correct place value column when adding. Some pupils may tend to place the number starting from the thousands place. E.g. 4025 + 364 may be written as:
```
   4025
 +  364
 _____
```

Learning objectives: Addition with regrouping in hundreds

Pupils will be able to:

- add two 4-digit numbers with regrouping in hundreds using concrete representations
- show regrouping of hundreds to thousands and hundreds
- carry out column addition by adding the hundreds first, then the thousands with regrouping in the hundreds place
- add without place value charts

Teaching sequence

- Use base ten equipment or counters to show the sum of 1200 and 2900 in a place value chart.
- Explain the procedures for adding 1200 and 2900 using base ten equipment or counters:

  Show regrouping in hundreds:
  2 hundreds + 9 hundreds
  = 11 hundreds
  = 1 thousand 1 hundred

  If necessary, show the addition using concrete representations.
- Guide pupils to see that the hundreds have been regrouped to make 1 thousand and 1 hundred.
- Next add the thousands.

  1 thousand + 2 thousands + 1 thousand = 4 thousands.
- Show the following working as a column addition:

$$
\begin{array}{r}
1200 \\
+\ 2900 \\
\hline
4100 \\
\hline
1
\end{array}
$$

Key concept

Addition with regrouping in hundreds

What you will need

- Base ten equipment
- Place value chart

Let's Learn!

Addition with regrouping in hundreds

1200   2900

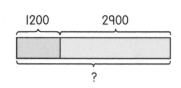

?

Thousands	Hundreds	Tens	Ones

First add the hundreds.

$$
\begin{array}{r}
1\ \boxed{2}\ 0\ 0 \\
+\ 2\ \boxed{9}\ 0\ 0 \\
\hline
\boxed{1}\ 0\ 0 \\
\hline
1
\end{array}
$$

2 hundreds + 9 hundreds = 11 hundreds = 1 thousand 1 hundred

Thousands	Hundreds	Tens	Ones

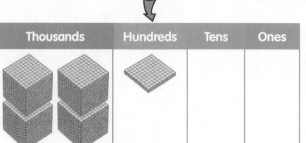

Then add the thousands.

$$
\begin{array}{r}
\boxed{1}\ 2\ 0\ 0 \\
+\ \boxed{2}\ 9\ 0\ 0 \\
\hline
4\ 1\ 0\ 0 \\
\hline
1
\end{array}
$$

The answer is 4100.

28

Additional activity

Ask pupils to work in pairs. Give some base ten equipment or counters to each pair. Ask pupils to take turns to show the addition of two 4-digit numbers involving regrouping in hundreds.

Thinking skills

- Applying place value relationships
- Identifying relationships

Addition of Numbers within 10 000 **Unit 2**

2 4500 + 3800 = ?

First add the hundreds and regroup.

5 hundreds + 8 hundreds = (13) hundreds

= (1) thousand (3) hundreds

Then add the thousands.

4 thousands + 3 thousands + (1) thousand

= (8) thousands

4500 + 3800 = (8300)

$$\begin{array}{r} 4\ 5\ 0\ 0 \\ +\ 3\ 8\ 0\ 0 \\ \hline 8300 \\ \hline \end{array}$$

3 Use a place value chart to help you add.

a
$$\begin{array}{r} 5\ 3\ 0\ 0 \\ +\ 1\ 9\ 0\ 0 \\ \hline 7200 \\ \hline \end{array}$$

b
$$\begin{array}{r} 2\ 8\ 0\ 0 \\ +\ 1\ 7\ 0\ 0 \\ \hline 4500 \\ \hline \end{array}$$

4 Find the sum of these numbers.

a   4800 and 4700 9500

b   4400 and 2700 7100

c   3500 and 5500 9000

5 Find the missing numbers.

a
$$\begin{array}{r} 2\ 4\ 7\ 3 \\ +\ 1\ 4\ 2\ (3) \\ \hline 3\ 8\ 9\ 6 \\ \hline \end{array}$$

b
$$\begin{array}{r} 4\ 5\ 6\ (4) \\ +\ 2\ 7\ 2\ 8 \\ \hline 7\ 2\ 9\ 2 \\ \hline \end{array}$$

29

Teaching sequence

- Using the same procedure, ask pupils to work on the sum given in the textbook, focusing on regrouping and place values.

- Ask pupils to work on the sums in vertical format.
- In this exercise, pupils are expected to convert the sums to vertical format and add.

- Relate 'sum' to the addition sums in this section.

- Pupils are expected to make some deductions in order to solve the problems.

What you will need

Hundreds cards from 100 to 900: three sets per group
(see Photocopy master 3 on page 263)

Additional activity

Ask pupils to work in groups of 4 to play a different game of 'Snap!' Use the same set of cards as in ⑥.

Player 1 shuffles the cards and deals four cards to each pupil. They place the remaining cards face down in a pile, in the middle of the group.

Player 1 turns over a card from the pile.

Players should call out 'Snap!' if the sum of their cards and this card is more than 1000.

The first player to call out 'Snap!' keeps the card from the pile.

Continue playing until there are no more cards left in the pile.

The player with the most cards wins.

Teaching sequence

⑥ *Game*

- The objective of the game is to encourage pupils to practise regrouping numbers from hundreds to thousands.
- Ask pupils to follow the steps in the textbook to play the game.

Game

⑥ **Snap a thousand!**

How to play:

Players: 2 to 4
You will need:
- hundreds cards from 100 to 900 (three sets)

1 Make hundreds cards from 100 to 900. Make three sets for each number.

2 Shuffle the cards. Each player picks six cards.

3 All players show one card at the same time. Check if any two of the cards shown add up to 1000.

Example 400 600
                1000

The player to call out "thousand snap" first can collect the two cards that make the thousand pair.

4 When no more thousand pairs can be found from the cards shown, all players will show another card and play on.

The player who collects the most thousand pairs is the winner.

5 The game ends when no more thousand pairs can be found.

30

Objective of activity

This task enables pupils to find out when regrouping in the hundreds place will occur.

Independent work

Practice 3 in Practice Book 3A, pp 29 to 30.

Additional activity

Ask pupils to work in pairs. Pupil A writes two 4-digit numbers similar to those on p 31 of the textbook. Pupil A then crosses out the digit in the hundreds place of one of the numbers. Pupil B finds all possible digits that will allow regrouping in hundreds when adding the two numbers.

Addition of Numbers within 10 000 **Unit 2**

Teaching sequence

7 *Let's Explore!*

- Ask pupils to work in pairs to think of digits that will let them regroup the hundreds in the addition sums.

- In each problem, they are expected to provide different answers to produce the same result.

  This activity serves the same purpose as **5** but it is more challenging.

Let's Explore!

7 For each sum, find a number that can be regrouped in hundreds. Then add the numbers.

```
  4 2 0 0
+ 2 ? 0 0
```

If you put 1, 2, 3, 4, 5, 6 or 7 in the box, you do not need to regroup the hundreds. Try using 8 or 9.

Example using the digit '8'

```
  4 2 0 0
+ 2 8 0 0
      0 0 0
    1
```
Using the digit '8', add the hundreds first.

```
  4 2 0 0
+ 2 8 0 0
  7 0 0 0
  1
```
Then add the thousands. We get 7000.

Example using the digit '9'

```
  4 2 0 0
+ 2 9 0 0
    1 0 0
  1
```
Using the digit '9', add the hundreds first.

The number can be 8 or 9!

```
  4 2 0 0
+ 2 9 0 0
  7 1 0 0
  1
```
Then add the thousands. We get 7100.

a
```
  5 (4) 0 0
+ 2  6  0 0
    8000
```

b
```
  2 4 0 0
+ 3 (6) 0 0
    6000
```
Answers vary

c
```
  6  8  0 0
+ 2 (2) 0 0
    9000
```
Practice Book 3A, p.29

31

Learning objectives: Addition with regrouping in ones, tens and hundreds

Pupils will be able to:

- add two 4-digit numbers with regrouping in ones, tens and hundreds using concrete representations
- show regrouping of ones to tens and ones; tens to hundreds and tens; hundreds to thousands and hundreds
- carry out column addition with regrouping in the ones, tens and hundreds places
- solve addition word problems with regrouping by using concrete representations

Key concept

Addition with regrouping in ones, tens and hundreds

Thinking skills

- Applying place value relationships
- Translating words to symbols
- Analysing

What you will need

- Base ten equipment
- Place value charts

Teaching sequence

- Review regrouping concepts, using base ten equipment as concrete representations: '10 ones = 1 ten', '10 tens = 1 hundred' and '10 hundreds = 1 thousand'.
- Demonstrate how to add 1153 and 4959 using base ten equipment in a place value chart.
- Revise the strategy for addition by adding numbers from right to left.
- Demonstrate addition procedures with regrouping in ones, tens and hundreds.
- Add the ones:
  3 ones + 9 ones = 12 ones
  = 1 ten 2 ones
- Then add the tens:
  5 tens + 5 tens + 1 ten
  = 11 tens = 1 hundred 1 ten

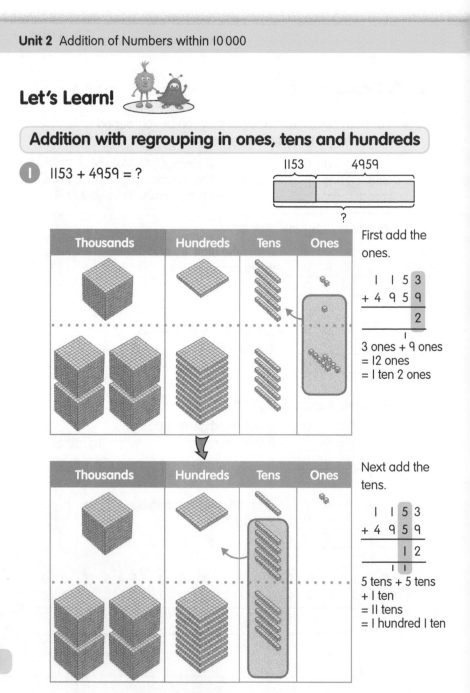

Additional activity

Ask pupils to work in pairs. Each pupil writes two 4-digit numbers that require regrouping when added. Each pupil then checks their partner's answers.

Teaching sequence

- Then add the hundreds:
  9 hundreds + 1 hundred +
  1 hundred = 11 hundreds
  = 1 thousand 1 hundred
- Finally add the thousands:
  4 thousands + 1 thousand +
  1 thousand = 6 thousands

  1153 + 4959 = 6112

  Show the working as a column addition.

2

- Encourage pupils to practise addition of numbers with regrouping in ones, tens and hundreds.

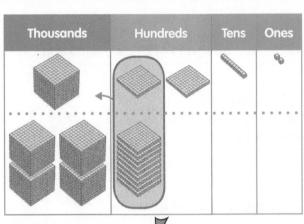

Thousands	Hundreds	Tens	Ones

Then add the hundreds.

```
  1 1 5 3
+ 4 9 5 9
---------
    1 1 2
  1 1 1
```

1 hundred + 9 hundreds
+ 1 hundred
= 11 hundreds
= 1 thousand 1 hundred

Thousands	Hundreds	Tens	Ones

Now add the thousands.

```
  1 1 5 3
+ 4 9 5 9
---------
  6 1 1 2
  1 1 1
```

1 thousand + 4 thousands
+ 1 thousand = 6 thousands

The answer is 6112.

2 Use place value charts to help you add.

a
```
  4 2 1 7
+ 3 1 9 5
```
[7412]

b
```
  2 7 6 4
+ 5 4 8 3
```
[8247]

c
```
  3 6 2 8
+ 1 7 9 5
```
[5423]

d
```
  2 3 4 8
+ 1 1 5 3
```
[3501]

e
```
  7 1 7 6
+ 1 8 4 0
```
[9016]

f
```
  5 3 4 8
+ 3 7 9 2
```
[9140]

33

Practice 4 in Practice Book 3A,
pp 31 to 34.

Teaching sequence

3

- Remind pupils of the meaning of sum, and ask them to work on these addition problems accordingly.

4 and **5**

- Ask pupils to work on the addition word problems with or without regrouping.
- Pupils should recognise that the following concepts are used: 'adding on' and 'comparing' concepts in addition.

Unit 2 Addition of Numbers within 10 000

3 Find the sum of:

a 2479 and 1326   **b** 3562 and 4729   **c** 6185 and 2847
3805   8291   9032

4 The population of a town is 7325.
2501 more people move to the town.
How many people live there now?

7325 (+) 2501 = 9826

There are 9826 people living in the town now.

5 Tom makes 4728 bread rolls.
Jess makes 1584 more bread rolls than Tom.
How many bread rolls does Jess make?

4728 (+) 1584 = 6312

Jess makes 6312 bread rolls.

Practice Book 3A, p.31

34

Objectives of activity

Pupils will be able to:

- identify two common mistakes made in the addition of two numbers and to explain the mistakes.
- express their understanding of regrouping by writing down the steps in the procedure for adding two numbers.

Additional activity

Ask pupils to work in pairs. Each pupil writes a sum in vertical format containing two 4-digit numbers, and shows the correct answer. Each pupil then changes one of the digits to introduce a mistake. Pupils check each other's work and spot the mistakes.

Maths Journal

6 **Example**

Hardeep spotted some mistakes in these questions.

```
  3 4 6 7
+ 1 9 3 2
---------
  4 3 9 9
```

```
  7 5 2 9
+ 2 4 6 1
---------
  9 9 8 0
```

The hundreds were not regrouped into thousands and hundreds.

The ones were not regrouped into tens and ones.

a Here are some mistakes. Write down what has been done incorrectly and ask your friend to check.

```
  5 8 6 9
+ 1 4 2 5
---------
  4 4 4 4
```
Subtracted instead of adding

```
  3 5 7 3
+ 1 6 4 5
---------
  4 1 1 8
```
Did not regroup when necessary

Example

Millie wrote down the steps for adding these two numbers.

```
  2 3 4
+ 4 7 5
-------
  7 0 9
```

Step 1: Add 4 ones and 5 ones to get 9 ones.

Step 2: Add 3 tens and 7 tens to get 10 tens.

Step 3: Regroup 10 tens into 1 hundred and 0 tens.

Step 4: Add 2 hundreds, 4 hundreds and 1 hundred to get 7 hundreds.

b Write down the steps for adding these two numbers.

```
  4 2 6 7
+ 2 9 1 5
---------
  7182
```

Step 1: Add 7 ones and 5 ones to get 12 ones.
Step 2: Regroup 12 ones into 1 ten and 2 ones.
Step 3: Add 6 tens, 1 ten and 1 ten to get 8 tens.
Step 4: Add 2 hundreds and 9 hundreds to get 11 hundreds.
Step 5: Regroup 11 hundreds into 1 thousand and 1 hundred.
Step 6: Add 4 thousands, 2 thousands and 1 thousand to get 7 thousands.

35

Teaching sequence

6 *Maths Journal*

a

- This activity involves identifying mistakes in addition with regrouping.
- Point out the two examples in the textbook that are incorrect. Ask pupils to explain why the answers are not correct and ask them to work out the correct answers.
- Ask pupils to find the mistakes in the two column additions, then to work out the correct answers.

b

- This activity helps pupils to reflect on the procedures for adding numbers with regrouping.
- Ask pupils to use the example that shows the steps for addition to write down the steps for adding 4267 and 2915.

Objective of activity

These questions reinforce and consolidate the process of regrouping hundreds.

Thinking skills

- Comparing
- Analysing parts and whole

Independent work

Challenging Practice, Problem Solving and Review I in Practice Book 3A, pp 35 to 42.

Teaching sequence

7 *Put On Your Thinking Caps!*

- Pupils should use deduction to solve the problems.
- Encourage pupils to apply regrouping from hundreds to thousands.

Put On Your Thinking Caps!

7 **a** Find the missing number.

```
    2  6  4  3
+   2  6  4  3
─────────────
    5 (2) 8  6
```

The number is 2.

b Find a number that **will not** allow regrouping of the hundreds.
Then add.

```
    4 (0) 0  0            5  6  0  0
+   3  7  0  0        +   2 (0) 0  0
─────────────            ─────────────
     7700                     7600
```

Answers vary

c Find a number that **will** allow regrouping of the hundreds.
Then add.

```
    7 (7) 0  0            4  2  0  0
+   1  3  0  0        +   3 (8) 0  0
─────────────            ─────────────
     9000                     8000
```

Answers vary

Practice Book 3A, p.35   Practice Book 3A, p.37

36

Unit 2 Addition of Numbers within 10 000

Date: _____

Practice I The meaning of sum

1 Add.

a
```
   7 1
 + 1 8
 ─────
   8 9
```

b
```
   6 8
 + 2 4
 ─────
   9 2
```

c
```
   1 5 3
 +   7 9
 ───────
   2 3 2
```

d
```
   2 0 7
 + 1 9 5
 ───────
   4 0 2
```

2 Fill in the spaces.

Example Find the sum of 96 and 73.

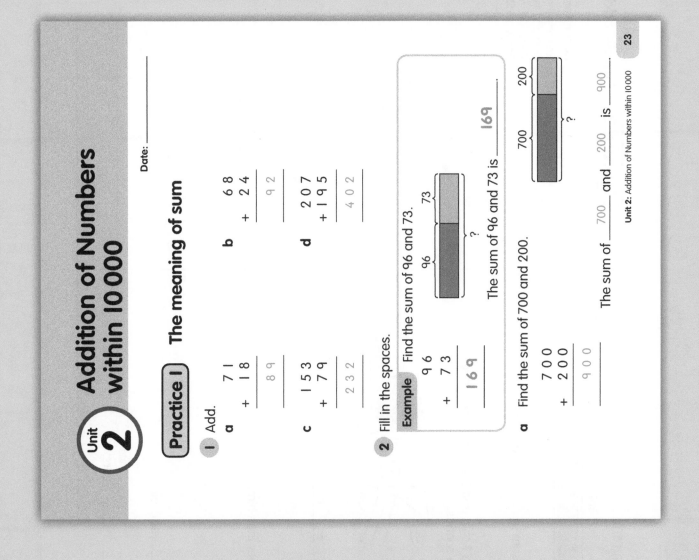

```
    9 6
 +  7 3
 ─────
  1 6 9
```

The sum of 96 and 73 is ___169___.

a Find the sum of 700 and 200.

```
   7 0 0
 + 2 0 0
 ───────
   9 0 0
```

The sum of ___700___ and ___200___ is ___900___.

23

Practice 2   Simple addition within 10 000

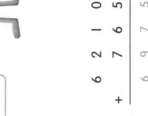

Remember:
First add the ones.
Next add the tens.
Then add the hundreds.
Finally add the thousands.

1 Add the numbers.

Example
```
    5 0 8
  +   9 1
  -------
    9 9 9
```

a
```
    6 2 1 0
  +   7 6 5
  ---------
    6 9 7 5
```

b
```
    5 3 2 4
  + 3 3 5 1
  ---------
    8 6 7 5
```

c
```
    5 4 1 3
  + 1 3 8 2
  ---------
    6 7 9 5
```

d
```
    7 3 6 3
  + 1 4 0 6
  ---------
    8 7 6 9
```

e
```
    1 0 4 8
  + 3 4 3 0
  ---------
    4 4 7 8
```

---

b Find the sum of 215 and 507.

```
    2 1 5
  + 5 0 7
  -------
    7 2 2
```

215   507

?

The sum of 215 and 507 is 722.

3 Tai's dad spends £27 on a T-shirt and £120 on a pair of trainers.
Find the sum of money he spends.

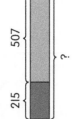 

27 + 120 = 147

The sum Tai's dad spends is £147.

4 Harry is 12 years old.
His sister is 3 years younger than him.
How old is Harry's sister?
Find the sum of their ages.

12 − 3 = 9

Harry's sister is 9 years old.

12 + 9 = 21

The sum of their ages is 21 years.

3 Use place value charts to help you find the answers.

a The sum of 6324 and 251 is [6575].

6324 + 251 = 6575

b The sum of 8624 and 1362 is [9986].

8624 + 1362 = 9986

c The sum of 3452 and 5037 is [8489].

3452 + 5037 = 8489

d 4632 + 5306 = [9938]

e 4514 + 1273 = [5787]

---

2 Add.

Example

1854 + 120 = [1974]

```
  1 8 5 4
+   1 2 0
  1 9 7 4
```

a 5362 + 506 = [5868]

b 741 + 2100 = [2841]

c 6542 + 3050 = [9592]

Practice 3 Addition with regrouping in hundreds

1 Use place value charts to help you add.

a
```
  5 3 0 0
+ 2 8 0 0
---------
  8 1 0 0
```

b
```
  7 6 0 0
+ 1 7 0 0
---------
  9 3 0 0
```

c
```
  6 5 0 0
+ 2 9 0 0
---------
  9 4 0 0
```

d
```
  3 8 0 0
+ 2 8 0 0
---------
  6 6 0 0
```

e
```
  3 7 0 0
+ 2 5 0 0
---------
  6 2 0 0
```

f
```
  2 6 0 0
+ 6 4 0 0
---------
  9 0 0 0
```

g
```
  1 1 0 0
+ 5 9 0 0
---------
  7 0 0 0
```

h
```
  4 9 0 0
+ 3 3 0 0
---------
  8 2 0 0
```

---

4 Add.

a 3361 + 2   = 3363 [d]
b 2516 + 3   = 2519 [r]
c 3005 + 4   = 3009 [e]
d 6019 + 20   = 6039 [l]
e 2020 + 73   = 2093 [c]
f 9600 + 300   = 9900 [o]
g 2468 + 500   = 2968 [i]
h 2500 + 273   = 2773 [p]
i 4376 + 3000   = 7376 [n]
j 2070 + 1020   = 3090 [d]

Farha and Ruby see lots of animals at the wildlife park. Find two of these animals by using your answers to fill in the spaces.

l	i	o	n
6039	2968	9900	7376

and

c	r	o	c	o	d	i	l	e
2093	2519	9900	2093	9900	3363	2968	6039	3009

5 Answer these questions.

a 4132 + 624 = 4756
b 5051 + 2136 = 7187
c 7423 + 1362 = 8785
d 8999 + 1000 = 9999

Practice 4 Addition with regrouping in ones, tens and hundreds

1 Follow the steps to add.
Fill in the spaces.

Step 1:

```
    5 5 3 2
 +  2 9 8 9
 _____
          1
```

Add the ones and regroup the ones.

2 ones + 9 ones = __11__ ones

= __1__ ten __1__ one

Step 2:

```
    5 5 3 2
 +  2 9 8 9
 _____
        2 1
```

Add the tens and regroup the tens.

3 tens + 8 tens + 1 ten = __12__ tens

= __1__ hundred __2__ tens

Step 3:

```
    5 5 3 2
 +  2 9 8 9
 _____
      5 2 1
```

Add the hundreds and regroup the hundreds.

5 hundreds + 9 hundreds + 1 hundred

= __15__ hundreds

= __1__ thousand __5__ hundreds

Step 4:

```
    5 5 3 2
 +  2 9 8 9
 _____
    8 5 2 1
```

Add the thousands.

5 thousands + 2 thousands + 1 thousand

= __8__ thousands

2 Add.

a 1730 + 2604

= 4334

b 1836 + 2801

= 4637

c 3610 + 5927

= 9537

d 1900 + 7511

= 9411

e 5516 + 2883

= 8399

f 6325 + 1931

= 8256

2 Answer these questions.

a
```
   8 9 7
+  9 2 2
---------
 1 8 1 9
```

b
```
   2 1 5
+  7 9 6
---------
 1 0 1 1
```

c
```
   6 5 7
+  9 4 3
---------
 1 6 0 0
```

d
```
 1 0 6 6
+  7 5 3
---------
 1 8 1 9
```

e
```
 1 1 9 8
+  6 2 2
---------
 1 8 2 0
```

f
```
 3 3 2 9
+ 1 5 9 7
---------
 4 9 2 6
```

g
```
 6 2 5 8
+ 2 9 3 7
---------
 9 1 9 5
```

h
```
 3 9 1 4
+    8 6
---------
 4 0 0 0
```

i
```
 3 6 7 4
+ 1 6 6 7
---------
 5 3 4 1
```

j
```
 6 4 3 5
+ 2 6 8 9
---------
 9 1 2 4
```

3

A baker makes 3452 custard tarts in the morning.
He makes another 759 custard tarts in the afternoon.
How many custard tarts does the baker make altogether?

Bar model: 3452 custard tarts | 759 custard tarts — ?

$3452 + 759 = 4211$

The baker makes ___4211___ custard tarts altogether.

4

The supermarket sells 6835 apples and 2795 oranges.
How many pieces of fruit does the supermarket sell altogether?

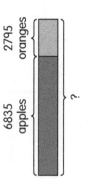

Bar model: 6835 apples | 2795 oranges — ?

$6835 + 2795 = 9630$

The supermarket sells ___9630___ pieces of fruit altogether.

Challenging Practice

1 a Make as many 4-digit numbers as possible using the digits in the box.
Do not begin with '0'. For each number, use each digit only once.

3	5	9	2	0	7

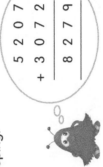

Answers vary

b Pick any two of these 4-digit numbers that you can add without regrouping.

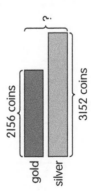

```
    5 2 0 7
  + 3 0 7 2
  ─────────
    8 2 7 9
```

Now you try it!   Answers vary

Answers vary

---

5 A theatre sold 5268 concert tickets. There are 1952 tickets left.
How many tickets did the theatre have to begin with?

5268 concert tickets   1952 concert tickets   ?

5268 + 1952 = 7220

The theatre had ___7220___ concert tickets to begin with.

6 Mrs Williams works at a bank.
She counts 2156 gold coins and 3152 silver coins today.
How many coins does she count altogether?

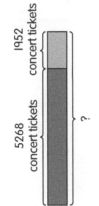

gold 2156 coins
silver 3152 coins   ?

2156 + 3152 = 5308

She counts ___5308___ coins altogether.

c Pick any two 4-digit numbers that you need to regroup to add.

$$\begin{array}{r} 2\ 7\ 9\ 3 \\ +\ 5\ 0\ 3\ 2 \\ \hline 7\ 8\ 2\ 5 \end{array}$$

Now you try it! *Answers vary*

2 Write a 4-digit number.
Add a number to it so that you have to regroup the ones, tens and hundreds.

Example

$$\begin{array}{r} 3\ 4\ 5\ 6 \\ +\ \ \ 6\ 8\ 7 \\ \hline 4\ 1\ 4\ 3 \end{array}$$

$+$ _____
Answers vary

Problem Solving

1 a Think of two numbers that add up to 100.

_____ + _____ = 100 *Answers vary*

b Think of three numbers that add up to 150.

_____ + _____ + _____ = 150 *Answers vary*

2 Find the missing numbers.

a
$$\begin{array}{r} 3\ 6\ 2\ 5 \\ +\ 2\ 2\ \boxed{6}\ 4 \\ \hline 5\ 8\ 8\ 9 \end{array}$$

b
$$\begin{array}{r} 2\ \boxed{4}\ 8\ 8 \\ +\ 3\ 6\ 1\ 5 \\ \hline 6\ 1\ 0\ 3 \end{array}$$

3 Ruby turns the pages of a book she is reading.

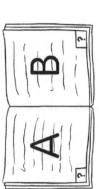

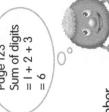

Page 123
Sum of digits
= 1 + 2 + 3
= 6

Each of the pages has a 3-digit page number.
The digits on page A add up to 7.
The digits on page B add up to 8.
What are two possible page numbers? _____ *Answers vary*

Date: _____

1 Fill in the missing numbers.

a 5216, 6216, 7216, _8216_, _____, 9216

b ___9, ___109, _____, 209, 309, 409

c 6029, 6019, 6009, _5999_, _____, 5989

2 Write in numbers.

a two thousand and twelve _2012_

b nine thousand and one _9001_

c six thousand, four hundred and twenty-one _6421_

3 Write the numbers in words.

a 9999 _nine thousand, nine hundred and ninety-nine_

b 1047 _one thousand and forty-seven_

c 6005 _six thousand and five_

4 Omar is given four digits.

The digit in is greater than each of the three other digits but is smaller than the sum of the three other digits.

a What is the greatest possible digit? _7_

b Using the digits above and the answer you found in **a**, help Omar to make:
- the greatest possible 4-digit number _7431_
- the smallest possible 4-digit number. _1347_

c What is the sum of the 4-digit numbers you found in **b**?

_7431 + 1347 = 8778_

4 Fill in the spaces.

a $4532 = 4000 + \underline{500} + 30 + 2$

b $1000, \underline{40}$ and 5 make 1045.

5 Circle the greatest number and cross out the smallest number.

~~7028~~, 7218, ⑦⑨⓪⓪ 7900, 7803

6 Complete the number patterns.

a 9335, 9235, 9135, $\underline{9035}$, $\underline{8935}$

b 21, $\underline{1021}$, $\underline{2021}$, 3021, 4021

7 Add.

a
```
    6 3 0 5
  + 2 5 1 2
  ---------
    8 8 1 7
```

b
```
    3 5 0 0
  + 2 8 0 0
  ---------
    6 3 0 0
```

c
```
    4 2 6 5
  + 2 0 5 8
  ---------
    6 3 2 3
```

d
```
    4 6 7 2
  + 3 5 7 9
  ---------
    8 2 5 1
```

8 Find the values. Then arrange them in order. Begin with the smallest.

a 300 more than 6586 is $\underline{6886}$.

b 5000 less than 9702 is $\underline{4702}$.

c 8 more than 6580 is $\underline{6588}$.

smallest $\underline{4702}$, $\underline{6588}$, $\underline{6886}$

9 Fill in the spaces.

a ① ④ ⑦ ⑥

Use the digits above to make:

the greatest 4-digit number $\underline{7641}$

the smallest 4-digit number $\underline{1467}$

b Find the sum of the two numbers in **a** above. $\underline{9108}$

10 Answer these questions.

a Write a number that is greater than 3984 but smaller than 4000. $\underline{\text{Answers vary}}$

b Write a number that is greater than 6453 but smaller than 7148. $\underline{\text{Answers vary}}$

11 Use the clues to make a number.

a
- This number has four digits.
- The value of the digit in the thousands place is 1000.
- The digit in the hundreds place is the greatest single digit.
- The value of the digit in the tens place is 20.
- The digit in the ones place is 0.

The number is ___1920___.

b
- This number has four digits.
- The digit 8 is in the hundreds place.
- The digit 1 is in the thousands place.
- The digit in the tens place has a value of 10.
- The digit in the ones place is the greatest one-digit number.

The number is ___1819___.

Unit 3: Subtraction of Numbers within 10 000

Week	Learning Objectives	Thinking Skills	Resources
4	**(1) The meaning of difference** Pupils will be able to: • interpret the difference between two numbers when subtracting the smaller number from the greater number • subtract two numbers within 10 000 with regrouping in the ones column • translate verbal statements and models to subtraction number sentences	• Identifying relationships • Translating words and models to symbols	• Pupil Textbook 3A, pp 37 to 39 • Practice Book 3A, pp 43 to 46 • Teacher's Guide 3A, pp 63 to 65
4	**(2) Simple subtraction within 10 000** Pupils will be able to: • subtract two 4-digit numbers without regrouping • use concrete representations to subtract without regrouping • use column subtraction by subtracting the digits in the ones place first, followed by the tens, then the hundreds and finally the thousands	• Comparing • Identifying relationships	• Pupil Textbook 3A, pp 40 to 41 • Practice Book 3A, pp 47 to 48 • Teacher's Guide 3A, pp 66 to 67

Unit 3: Subtraction of Numbers within 10 000

Medium-term plan

Week	Learning Objectives	Thinking Skills	Resources
4	**(3) Subtraction with regrouping in hundreds and thousands** Pupils will be able to: • subtract two 4-digit numbers with regrouping in hundreds and thousands • use concrete representations to subtract numbers with regrouping • show regrouping of thousands to thousands and hundreds • carry out column subtraction by first subtracting the ones, followed by the tens; then regroup the thousands and hundreds to subtract the hundreds and finally the thousands	• Comparing • Identifying place value relationships	• Pupil Textbook 3A, pp 42 to 44 • Practice Book 3A, pp 49 to 50 • Teacher's Guide 3A, pp 68 to 70
5	**(4) Subtraction with regrouping in ones, tens, hundreds and thousands** Pupils will be able to: • subtract two 4-digit numbers with regrouping in ones, tens, hundreds and thousands • use concrete representations to subtract numbers with regrouping • show regrouping of tens to tens and ones; hundreds to hundreds and tens; thousands to thousands and hundreds • carry out column subtraction by first subtracting the ones, followed by the tens, then the hundreds and finally the thousands	• Comparing • Identifying place value relationships	• Pupil Textbook 3A, pp 45 to 49 • Practice Book 3A, pp 51 to 56 • Teacher's Guide 3A, pp 71 to 75

Unit 3: Subtraction of Numbers within 10 000

Week	Learning Objectives	Thinking Skills	Resources
5	**(5) Subtraction with numbers that have zeros** Pupils will be able to: • subtract a 4-digit number from another 4-digit number that has zeros in the hundreds, tens and ones • translate verbal statements and models to subtraction number sentences • use concrete representations to show regrouping from thousands to hundreds, tens and ones • carry out column subtraction starting with the ones, tens, hundreds and thousands by regrouping • solve subtraction word problems involving numbers with zeros by drawing models	• Comparing • Identifying place value relationships • Translating words and models to symbols	• Pupil Textbook 3A, pp 50 to 54 • Practice Book 3A, pp 57 to 58 • Teacher's Guide 3A, pp 76 to 80
5	*Put On Your Thinking Caps!* These questions will reinforce and consolidate pupils' understanding of regrouping in the procedure for subtraction.	• Comparing Heuristic for problem solving: • Guess and check	• Pupil Textbook 3A, p 55 • Practice Book 3A, pp 59 to 62 • Teacher's Guide 3A, p 81

Subtraction of Numbers within 10 000

Learning objectives:
The meaning of difference

Pupils will be able to:

- interpret the difference between two numbers when subtracting the smaller number from the greater number

- subtract two numbers within 10 000 with regrouping in the ones column
- translate verbal statements and models to subtraction number sentences

Key concept

The regrouping concept in subtraction

Thinking skills
- Identifying relationships
- Translating words and models to symbols

Additional activity

Ask pupils to work with a partner to write two questions, e.g., find the difference between 243 and 67. Ask pupils to check each other's answers.

Teaching sequence

1

- Introduce and explain the word '**difference**'. To find the difference between two numbers, (e.g., "*What is the difference between 67 and 3?*") explain to pupils that they need to subtract.

- Explain how to find the difference between 67 and 80. Highlight the use of a comparison model to represent the difference between two numbers.

- Demonstrate the procedure to find the answer using column subtraction.

2

- Ask pupils to complete the exercises involving the word 'difference' in the textbook.

Unit 3 Subtraction of Numbers within 10 000

Let's Learn!

The meaning of difference

1

 I need to find the difference between 67 and 80. Is this the same as finding the sum?

No! To find the sum, we add. To find the difference, we subtract.

80

67   ?

$$\begin{array}{r} ^7 8\,^1 0 \\ -\ 6\ 7 \\ \hline 1\ 3 \end{array}$$

The **difference** between 67 and 80 is 13.

 Remember to subtract the smaller number from the greater number.

2 Find the difference between these numbers.

  a   23 and 19 4   **b**   68 and 76 8

  c   791 and 368 423   **d**   437 and 682 245

 Home Maths Remind your child to always subtract the smaller number from the greater number. To find the difference between 413 and 685, we do this: 685 – 413.

37

What you will need

- A piece of paper with six numbers
- Bingo board (see Photocopy master 4 on page 264)

Additional activity

Ask pupils to work in pairs. Give them a question like the one below:

$$
\begin{array}{r}
54 \\
-\ \text{1A} \\
\hline
3\text{B}
\end{array}
$$

Ask pupils to find all the possible digits that A and B could represent.

Teaching sequence

③ *Game*

- The objective of the game is to allow pupils to revise and practise regrouping of numbers from tens to ones.
- Ask pupils to follow the instructions for playing the game in the textbook.

Unit 3 Subtraction of Numbers within 10 000

Game

③ Subtraction bingo

Players: 2
You will need:
- a piece of paper with six numbers
- bingo card

How to play:

1 Write these numbers on a piece of paper:
13, 101, 49, 39, 65 and 81.

2 Player 1 chooses two numbers from the piece of paper.

3 Player 1 finds the difference between the two numbers and marks their answer on the bingo card.

4 Players take turns to choose numbers from the list and mark their answers. Player 1 crosses their correct answers. Player 2 circles their correct answers.

5 The first player to get three ✗s or three ○s in a straight or diagonal line (↔, ↕ or ⤢) on the bingo card wins.

38

Independent work

Practice I in Practice Book 3A, pp 43 to 46.

Additional activity

Ask pupils to work in pairs. Show this model to pupils.

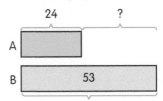

Ask each pair to write a word problem based on this model.

4 Solve these word problems.

a Mr Green sold 84 fish.
Mr Brown sold 56 fish.
What is the difference between the number of fish they sold?

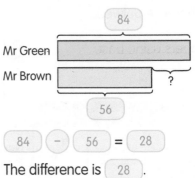

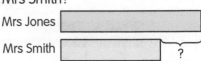

The difference is 28.

b Mrs Smith plants 274 apple trees in her orchard.
Mrs Jones plants 482 apple trees in her orchard.
How many more apple trees does Mrs Jones plant than Mrs Smith?

Mrs Jones [   ]

Mrs Smith [   ] ?

482 – 274 = 208
Mrs Jones plants 208 more apple trees than Mrs Smith.

c Tom baked 308 loaves of bread.
Mary baked 279 loaves of bread.
Find the difference between the number of loaves baked.

29 loaves of bread

Home Maths

Remind your child that when there is a zero in the greater number, we need to regroup before we subtract. For example, for 60 – 12, we regroup 6 tens into 5 tens and 10 ones before subtracting.

$$\begin{array}{r} 5\,6\,{}^{1}0 \\ -\ 1\ 2 \\ \hline 4\ 8 \end{array}$$

Practice Book 3A, p.43

39

Teaching sequence

4

a

- Ask pupils to read the word problem and identify the word 'difference' to realise that it involves subtraction. Relate this concept to the comparison model to help them solve the problem.

b

- Guide pupils to relate the data to the given model and to solve the problem.

c

- Ask pupils to read the word problem and draw a model to solve it.

Learning objectives:
Simple subtraction within 10 000

Pupils will be able to:

- subtract two 4-digit numbers without regrouping
- use concrete representations to subtract without regrouping
- use column subtraction by subtracting the digits in the ones place first, followed by the tens, then hundreds and finally the thousands

Key concept

Subtraction without regrouping

Thinking skills

- Comparing
- Identifying relationships

What you will need

- Base ten equipment or counters
- Place value charts

Teaching sequence

- Use base ten equipment to represent 5478 and 1254 in a place value chart.
- Introduce the strategy and procedure for subtracting numbers: from right to left (first subtract the ones, then the tens and hundreds and finally the thousands).
- Use base ten equipment to demonstrate how to subtract 1254 from 5478 in a place value chart.
- Explain column subtraction beginning with the ones, followed by the tens, then the hundreds and finally the thousands.
- Demonstrate the procedure to subtract using column subtraction without regrouping.

Unit 3 Subtraction of Numbers within 10 000

Let's Learn!

Simple subtraction within 10 000

1. Ella needs to find the difference between 5478 and 1254.
   She represents the numbers using base ten equipment.
   5478 – 1254 = ?

Thousands	Hundreds	Tens	Ones

Thousands	Hundreds	Tens	Ones

When we subtract 1254 from 5478, we get 4224.

First subtract the ones.

```
  5 4 7 8
- 1 2 5 4
---------
        4
```

Next subtract the tens.

```
  5 4 7 8
- 1 2 5 4
---------
      2 4
```

Then subtract the hundreds.

```
  5 4 7 8
- 1 2 5 4
---------
    2 2 4
```

Finally subtract the thousands.

```
  5 4 7 8
- 1 2 5 4
---------
  4 2 2 4
```

Subtraction of Numbers within 10 000 **Unit 3**

2 The difference between 7526 and 2103 is (5423).

Thousands	Hundreds	Tens	Ones
7	5	2	6
− 2	1	0	3
(5)	(4)	(2)	(3)

3 Subtract.

a
```
  2 3 5 6
− 1 2 4 3
```
(1113)

b
```
  3 4 1 8
− 3 1 0 2
```
(316)

c
```
  9 8 3 2
− 7 8 1 0
```
(2022)

Activity

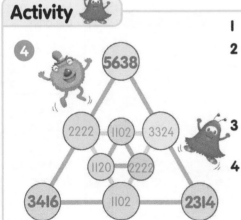

1   Copy the diagram.

2   Choose two numbers from the circles. Subtract the smaller number from the greater number.

3   Write the answer in the circle between the two numbers.

4   Repeat steps **2** and **3** until you have filled in all the circles.

Practice Book 3A, p.47

Talk to your child about how we write down subtraction problems like this one:

Home
Maths
```
  2 4 8              2 4 8
− 2 3 4   is written as  − 2 3 4
  0 1 4    ────────→     1 4
```
↑
This zero is not written down.

41

Teaching sequence

2

- Ask pupils to work on the subtraction using a place value chart.
- In this exercise, pupils are guided by a place value chart.

3

- Ask pupils to complete the exercises without using concrete representations or a place value chart.

4

- This activity reinforces pupils' understanding of the concept and strategy for subtraction.

Learning objectives: Subtraction with regrouping in hundreds and thousands

Pupils will be able to:

- subtract two 4-digit numbers with regrouping in hundreds and thousands
- use concrete representations to subtract numbers with regrouping
- show regrouping of thousands to thousands and hundreds

- carry out column subtraction by first subtracting the ones, followed by the tens; then regroup the thousands and hundreds to subtract the hundreds and finally the thousands

Key concept

Regrouping from thousands to hundreds

Thinking skills

- Comparing
- Identifying place value relationships

What you will need

- Base ten equipment
- Place value charts

Teaching sequence

- Use concrete representations and the model drawing to explain the subtraction statement.
- Explain how to regroup in thousands, hundreds, tens and ones:

  1 thousand = 10 hundreds;

  3 thousands
  = 2 thousands 10 hundreds;

  2 thousands 4 tens
  = 1 thousand 10 hundreds
    + 4 tens
  = 1 thousand 104 tens

- Explain the strategy for subtraction: subtract from right to left.
- Highlight to pupils that in this question, it was not necessary to regroup from hundreds to tens and from tens to ones.

Unit 3 Subtraction of Numbers within 10 000

Let's Learn!

Subtraction with regrouping in hundreds and thousands

1 4249 − 1926 = ?

4249

1926   ?

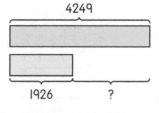

Thousands	Hundreds	Tens	Ones

First subtract the ones.

```
    4 2 4 9
  − 1 9 2 6
  ─────────
          3
```

9 ones − 6 ones
= 3 ones

Next subtract the tens.

```
    4 2 4 9
  − 1 9 2 6
  ─────────
        2 3
```

4 tens − 2 tens
= 2 tens

42

Additional activity

Ask pupils to work in pairs. Ask each pupil to show the following using base ten equipment or counters:

(a) 4500 – 2700

(b) 8200 – 3900

Ask pupils to check each other's answers.

We can't subtract 9 hundreds from 2 hundreds, so we regroup the thousands and the hundreds.

Thousands	Hundreds	Tens	Ones

Regroup.

4 thousands
2 hundreds
= 3 thousands
  12 hundreds

Thousands	Hundreds	Tens	Ones
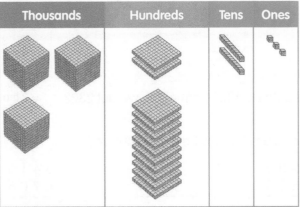			

4 thousands 2 hundreds is regrouped as
3 thousands 12 hundreds.

43

Teaching sequence

- Explain regrouping from thousands to hundreds.
- Follow the procedure to complete the subtraction.

  4249 – 1926 = 2323

- Demonstrate to pupils how to subtract in columns by first subtracting the ones, followed by the tens. Next regroup the thousands and hundreds, and then subtract the hundreds and finally the thousands.

Ask pupils to work in pairs. Each pupil should tell their partner a number story based on one of the questions. Ask pupils to present their number stories and then solve them. Encourage pupils to write more than one number story for each question.

Additional activity

Show pupils this:

$$
\begin{array}{r}
3478 \\
- \ 1752 \\
\hline
2326
\end{array}
$$

Ask pupils if the working is correct. Ask them to explain why they think it is correct or incorrect. This will help you to assess their ability to subtract with regrouping.

Independent work

Practice 3 in Practice Book 3A, pp 49 to 50.

Teaching sequence

- Ask pupils to work on this question. Use it to check pupils' understanding of regrouping of thousands to thousands and hundreds.

Unit 3 Subtraction of Numbers within 10 000

Thousands	Hundreds	Tens	Ones

Then subtract the hundreds.

$$
\begin{array}{r}
^3\!4 \ ^12 \ 4 \ 9 \\
- \ 1 \ 9 \ 2 \ 6 \\
\hline
3 \ 2 \ 3
\end{array}
$$

12 hundreds
− 9 hundreds
= 3 hundreds

Thousands	Hundreds	Tens	Ones

Finally subtract the thousands.

$$
\begin{array}{r}
^3\!4 \ ^12 \ 4 \ 9 \\
- \ 1 \ 9 \ 2 \ 6 \\
\hline
2 \ 3 \ 2 \ 3
\end{array}
$$

3 thousands
− 1 thousand
= 2 thousands

When we subtract 1926 from 4249, we get 2323.

2 Use place value charts to help you subtract.

a
$$
\begin{array}{r}
6 \ 2 \ 0 \ 0 \\
- \ \ \ 8 \ 0 \ 0 \\
\hline
5400
\end{array}
$$

b
$$
\begin{array}{r}
5 \ 1 \ 2 \ 6 \\
- \ 3 \ 4 \ 1 \ 2 \\
\hline
1714
\end{array}
$$

c
$$
\begin{array}{r}
8 \ 4 \ 1 \ 5 \\
- \ 6 \ 7 \ 0 \ 5 \\
\hline
1710
\end{array}
$$

44

Practice Book 3A, p.49

Learning objectives:
Subtraction with regrouping in ones, tens, hundreds and thousands

Pupils will be able to:

- subtract two 4-digit numbers with regrouping in ones, tens, hundreds and thousands
- use concrete representations to subtract numbers with regrouping
- show regrouping of tens to tens and ones; hundreds to hundreds and tens; thousands to thousands and hundreds

- carry out column subtraction by first subtracting the ones, followed by the tens, then the hundreds and finally the thousands

Key concept

Subtraction with regrouping in ones, tens, hundreds and thousands

Thinking skills

- Comparing
- Identifying place value relationships

What you will need

- Base ten equipment
- Place value charts

Teaching sequence

1

- Use concrete representations and the model drawing to explain the subtraction statement.
- Explain how to regroup in thousands, hundreds, tens and ones.

Let's Learn!

Subtraction with regrouping in ones, tens, hundreds and thousands

1 5146 − 2598 = ?

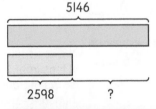

5146

2598   ?

> We can't subtract 8 ones from 6 ones, so we regroup the tens and ones.

Thousands	Hundreds	Tens	Ones

Regroup.

4 tens 6 ones
= 3 tens 16 ones

Thousands	Hundreds	Tens	Ones

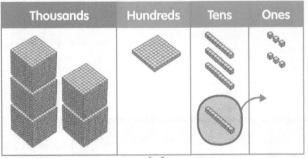

45

Teaching sequence

- Explain the strategy for subtraction: subtract from right to left.
- Highlight to pupils that in this question thousands were regrouped to hundreds, hundreds to tens and tens to ones.
- Follow the procedures to complete the subtraction.
- Highlight the following procedures:
  - (a) 4 tens 6 ones
    = 3 tens 16 ones
    Then use 16 ones to subtract 8 ones.

Unit 3 Subtraction of Numbers within 10 000

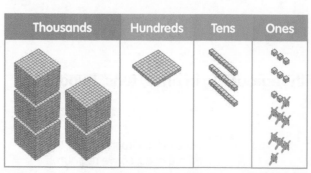

First subtract the ones.

$$
\begin{array}{r}
5\ 1\ \overset{3}{\cancel{4}}\ \overset{1}{6} \\
-\ 2\ 5\ 9\ 8 \\
\hline
8
\end{array}
$$

16 ones – 8 ones
= 8 ones

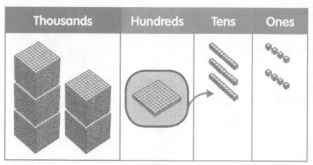

We can't subtract 9 tens from 3 tens, so we regroup the hundreds and tens.

Regroup.

I hundred 3 tens
= 0 hundreds 13 tens

46

Thousands	Hundreds	Tens	Ones

Next subtract the tens.

$$\begin{array}{r} 5\ \overset{0}{\cancel{}}\ \overset{13}{\cancel{4}}\ \overset{1}{6} \\ -\ 2\ 5\ 9\ 8 \\ \hline 4\ 8 \end{array}$$

13 tens – 9 tens = 4 tens

Thousands	Hundreds	Tens	Ones

We can't subtract 5 hundreds from 0 hundreds, so we regroup the thousands and hundreds.

Thousands	Hundreds	Tens	Ones

Regroup.

5 thousands
0 hundreds
= 4 thousands
   10 hundreds

47

(b) I hundred
= 0 hundreds 10 tens
10 tens + 3 tens = 13 tens
Then use 13 tens to
subtract 9 tens.

Additional activity

Show pupils the following and
ask them why it is incorrect.

$$
\begin{array}{r}
5726 \\
-\ 1947 \\
\hline
4221 \\
\hline
\end{array}
$$

Teaching sequence

(c) 5 thousands 0 hundreds
= 4 thousands 10 hundreds
Then use 10 hundreds to
subtract 5 hundreds.

- If necessary, use concrete
representations to show the
regrouping at each stage.

 2

- Ask pupils to use place value
charts to find the answers if
necessary.

 3

- Ask pupils to find the answers
to the column subtractions
without using concrete
representations.

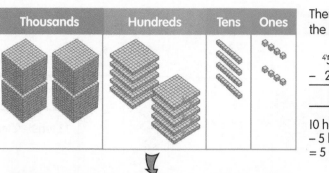

Unit 3 Subtraction of Numbers within 10 000

Thousands	Hundreds	Tens	Ones

Then subtract
the hundreds.

10 hundreds
– 5 hundreds
= 5 hundreds

Thousands	Hundreds	Tens	Ones

Finally subtract
the thousands.

4 thousands
– 2 thousands
= 2 thousands

When we subtract 2598 from 5146, we get 2548.

2 Use place value charts to help you subtract.

a
$$
\begin{array}{r}
5\ 1\ 7\ 6 \\
-\ 4\ 3\ 2\ 8 \\
\hline
\end{array}
$$
[848]

b
$$
\begin{array}{r}
6\ 4\ 5\ 9 \\
-\ 2\ 7\ 8\ 3 \\
\hline
\end{array}
$$
[3676]

c
$$
\begin{array}{r}
8\ 3\ 2\ 4 \\
-\ 5\ 7\ 8\ 6 \\
\hline
\end{array}
$$
[2538]

3 Subtract.

a
$$
\begin{array}{r}
8\ 2\ 4\ 0 \\
-\ 3\ 9\ 7\ 0 \\
\hline
\end{array}
$$
[4270]

b
$$
\begin{array}{r}
6\ 1\ 3\ 0 \\
-\ 2\ 5\ 8\ 0 \\
\hline
\end{array}
$$
[3550]

c
$$
\begin{array}{r}
9\ 1\ 6\ 4 \\
-\ 5\ 4\ 6\ 7 \\
\hline
\end{array}
$$
[3697]

d
$$
\begin{array}{r}
3\ 2\ 1\ 0 \\
-\ 1\ 7\ 8\ 9 \\
\hline
\end{array}
$$
[1421]

e
$$
\begin{array}{r}
2\ 3\ 1\ 0 \\
-\ 1\ 6\ 2\ 7 \\
\hline
\end{array}
$$
[683]

f
$$
\begin{array}{r}
4\ 6\ 9\ 2 \\
-\ 1\ 8\ 9\ 3 \\
\hline
\end{array}
$$
[2799]

48

What you will need

Number cards from 0 to 9:
four sets per group.
(see Photocopy master 5 on
page 265)

Independent work

Practice 4 in Practice Book 3A,
pp 51 to 56.

Teaching sequence

④ *Game*

- The objective of the activity is to encourage pupils to create their own questions and then practise subtracting numbers.
- Ask pupils to work in groups of 2 to 4. Each group should make four sets of number cards from 0 to 9. Ask pupils to follow the steps in the textbook to play the game.
- You may need to explain the strategy to help pupils get the smallest possible answer. Use a minuend that is as close to the subtrahend as possible. Do not accept '0' as an answer.

Game

④ **Go for the smallest!**

How to play:

Players: 2 to 4
You will need:
- number cards from 0 to 9 (four sets)

1 Make four sets of number cards from 0 to 9.

2 Shuffle the cards. Each player picks eight cards.

3 Arrange your cards to make two 4-digit numbers.

4 Subtract the numbers.

The player with the smallest answer wins!

Practice Book 3A, p.51

49

Learning objectives: Subtraction with numbers that have zeros

Pupils will be able to:

- subtract a 4-digit number from another 4-digit number that has zeros in the hundreds, tens and ones
- translate verbal statements and models to subtraction number sentences
- use concrete representations to show regrouping from thousands to hundreds, tens and ones

- carry out column subtraction starting with the ones, tens, hundreds and thousands by regrouping
- solve subtraction word problems involving numbers with zeros by drawing models

Thinking skills

- Comparing
- Identifying place value relationships
- Translating words and models to symbols

Key concept

Regrouping from thousands to hundreds, tens and ones in subtraction

Teaching sequence

- Use concrete representations to explain to pupils how to regroup 2 thousands by exchanging 1 thousand for 10 hundreds, 1 hundred for 10 tens and 1 ten for 10 ones.

  2 thousands = 1 thousand, 9 hundreds, 9 tens and 10 ones.

  Carry out the subtraction from right to left.

Unit 3 Subtraction of Numbers within 10 000

Let's Learn!

| Subtraction with numbers that have zeros |

① 2000 – 257 = ?

Thousands	Hundreds	Tens	Ones

Regroup the thousands and hundreds.

Regroup.

2 thousands
= 1 thousand
    10 hundreds

Thousands	Hundreds	Tens	Ones

Regroup the hundreds and tens.

Regroup.

10 hundreds
= 9 hundreds 10 tens

50

What you will need

Base ten equipment or counters

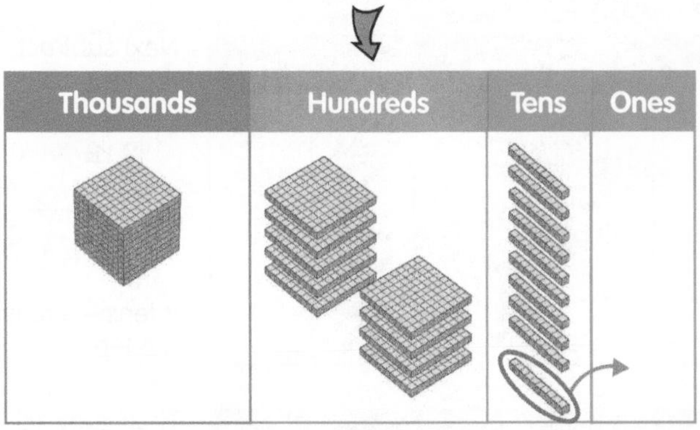

Thousands	Hundreds	Tens	Ones

Regroup the tens and ones.

Regroup.

10 tens = 9 tens 10 ones

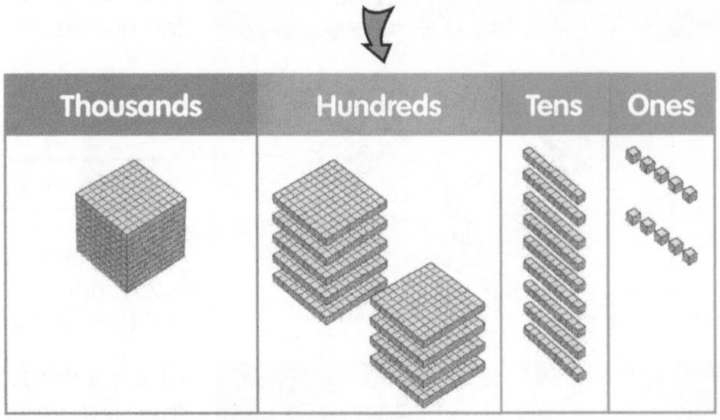

Thousands	Hundreds	Tens	Ones

2 thousands is regrouped as
1 thousand 9 hundreds 9 tens 10 ones.

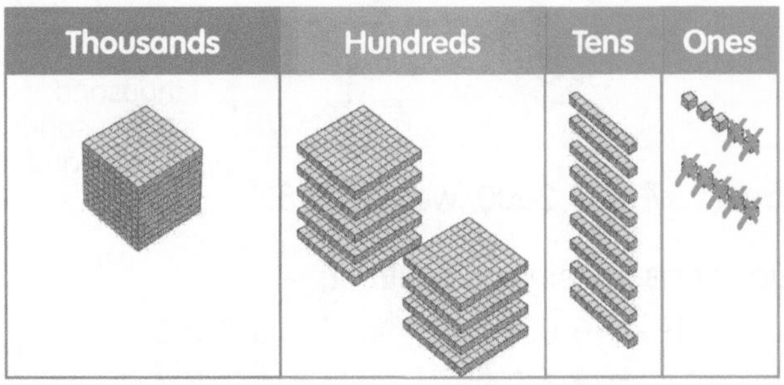

Thousands	Hundreds	Tens	Ones

First subtract the ones.

$$\begin{array}{r} {}^{1}\cancel{2}\,{}^{9}\cancel{0}\,{}^{9}\cancel{0}\,{}^{10}0 \\ -\quad 2\ 5\ 7 \\ \hline 3 \end{array}$$

10 ones − 7 ones
= 3 ones

51

Teaching sequence

- First subtract the ones.
  10 ones − 7 ones = 3 ones

Additional activity

Ask pupils to work in pairs.
Give some base ten equipment
or counters to each pair.
Encourage pupils to practise
regrouping using these concrete
representations.

Teaching sequence

Next subtract the tens.
9 tens – 5 tens = 4 tens
Then subtract the hundreds.
9 hundreds – 2 hundreds
= 7 hundreds
Finally subtract the thousands.
1 thousand – 0 thousands
= 1 thousand
2000 – 257 = 1743

- Demonstrate how to subtract
  in columns, starting with ones,
  tens, hundreds and thousands
  by regrouping.

- Ask pupils to work in pairs
  for **a**.
- If necessary, start with a
  concrete representation
  using base ten equipment or
  counters, followed by using a
  place value chart to subtract.
- Ask pupils to work on their
  own for **b** and **c**.

Unit 3 Subtraction of Numbers within 10 000

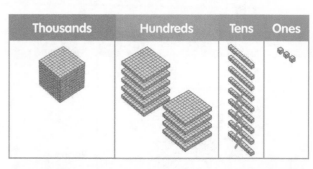

Next subtract
the tens.

$$
\begin{array}{r}
{}^{1}2\ {}^{9}\cancel{0}\ {}^{9}\cancel{0}\ {}^{1}0 \\
-\ \ \ \ 2\ \ 5\ \ 7 \\
\hline
4\ \ 3 \\
\end{array}
$$

9 tens – 5 tens
= 4 tens

Then subtract
the hundreds.

$$
\begin{array}{r}
{}^{1}2\ {}^{9}\cancel{0}\ {}^{9}\cancel{0}\ {}^{1}0 \\
-\ \ \ \ 2\ \ 5\ \ 7 \\
\hline
7\ \ 4\ \ 3 \\
\end{array}
$$

9 hundreds
– 2 hundreds
= 7 hundreds

Finally subtract
the thousands.

$$
\begin{array}{r}
{}^{1}2\ {}^{9}\cancel{0}\ {}^{9}\cancel{0}\ {}^{1}0 \\
-\ \ \ \ 2\ \ 5\ \ 7 \\
\hline
1\ \ 7\ \ 4\ \ 3 \\
\end{array}
$$

1 thousand
– 0 thousands
= 1 thousand

When we subtract 257 from 2000, we get 1743.

2 Use place value charts to help you subtract.

a	b	c
5 0 0 0	6 0 0 0	8 0 0 3
– 3 7 0 0	– 4 7 6 5	– 5 1 4 7
1300	1235	2856

52

What you will need

Card A and Card B
(see Photocopy master 6 on
page 266)

Additional activity

Ask pupils to work in pairs.
Each pupil writes a subtraction
question in vertical format.

E.g.,
$$
\begin{array}{r}
5432 \\
-\ 1765 \\
\hline
3667
\end{array}
$$

Pupils then cross out one digit of
a number and ask their partner
to find out what the
digit is.

Game

③ Subtract the numbers!

How to play:

Players: 2 to 4
You will need:
- Card A and Card B
for each pair

1 Work in pairs. Each pair
picks one number from
Card A and another
number from Card B.

2 Work as a pair to subtract
the smaller number from the
greater number.

Card A	Card B
126	1000
12	2000
1645	3000
3200	4000

3 Play four rounds and get
as many correct answers
as you can.

The pair with the most
correct answers wins!

Help your child work through subtraction of numbers with zeros using money,
for example: subtract 3p from 100p. Explain that the hundreds need to be
regrouped into tens and ones to find the correct answer.

$$
\begin{array}{r}
1\ \overset{9}{\cancel{0}}\ \overset{1}{0} \\
-\ \quad 3 \\
\hline
9\ 7
\end{array}
$$

53

Teaching sequence

③ Game

- This activity provides further
practice and helps pupils
to reinforce the concept of
regrouping before carrying
out subtraction.

Additional activity

Ask pupils to work in groups to write subtraction word problems involving money.

E.g., Mr Jones had £3000. He spent £596 on a television. How much did he have left? (taking away model)

E.g., Mrs Patel gave £1000 to charity. Mrs Williams gave £287 less than her. How much did Mrs Williams give to charity? (comparison model)

Independent work

Practice 5 in Practice Book 3A, pp 57 to 58.

Teaching sequence

4 and **5**

- Ask pupils to read and interpret the subtraction word problems. Then draw the model (comparison model), relating it to the context of the problem, and use it to solve the problem.

Unit 3 Subtraction of Numbers within 10 000

4 Farmer Jones picks 4000 apples from the trees in his orchard. Farmer Smith picks 935 fewer apples than Farmer Jones. How many apples does Farmer Smith pick?

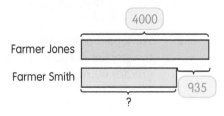

$$4000 - 935 = 3065$$

Farmer Smith picks 3065 apples.

5 A shop has 2000 pencils and 1726 notebooks. How many more pencils than notebooks does the shop have?

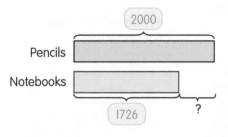

$$2000 - 1726 = 274$$

The shop has 274 more pencils than notebooks.

Practice Book 3A, p.57

54

Objective of activity
These questions will reinforce and consolidate pupils' understanding of regrouping in the procedure for subtraction.

Thinking skill
Comparing

Heuristic for problem solving
Guess and check

Independent work
Challenging Practice and *Problem Solving* in Practice Book 3A, pp 59 to 62.

Subtraction of Numbers within 10 000 **Unit 3**

Put On Your Thinking Caps!

6 Find the missing numbers.

a
```
    4  5  8  3
  - 1  7  2 (6)
  ──────────
    2  8  5  7
  ──────────
```

b
```
    7 (4) 5  1
  - 2  6  1  9
  ──────────
    4  8  3  2
```

c
```
   ( )  0  0  0
  - 2  6  4  3
  ──────────
    3  3  5  7
```
3357 + 2643 = 6000
The value in the box is 6.

Teaching sequence

6 *Put On Your Thinking Caps!*

• Explain the deduction method to solve the first problem.

  The following procedure can be used:
  Think aloud:
  "A number added on to 7 gives a number with 3 in the ones place.
  What could the number be?"
  Pupils may be able to see the context and work back to find the missing numbers.

• Encourage pupils to use a similar strategy to solve the other problems.

Practice Book 3A, p.59   Practice Book 3A, p.61

55

Unit 3: Subtraction of Numbers within 10 000   81

Unit 3

Subtraction of Numbers within 10 000

Date: _____

Practice 1   The meaning of difference

1. Find the difference.

a
```
   6 4
 – 1 2
 ─────
   5 2
```

b
```
   9 7
 – 1 7
 ─────
   8 0
```

c
```
   8 5
 – 8 2
 ─────
     3
```

d
```
   6 2
 – 1 8
 ─────
   4 4
```

e
```
   5 0
 – 4 7
 ─────
     3
```

f
```
   5 6 3
 – 4 2 6
 ───────
   1 3 7
```

g
```
   8 1 2
 – 6 3 1
 ───────
   1 8 1
```

h
```
   9 5 0
 – 1 7 8
 ───────
   7 7 2
```

i
```
   9 0 0
 – 2 5 6
 ───────
   6 4 4
```

2. Subtract.

a   78 – 42 = ___36___

b   656 – 214 = ___442___

4 Solve these word problems.

Example

Hardeep has 720 stickers and his brother has 690 stickers.
How many more stickers does Hardeep have than his brother?

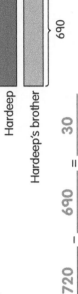

Hardeep — 720
Hardeep's brother — 690
?

720 − 690 = 30

Hardeep has __30__ more stickers than his brother.

5 Michael and Isabel go for a run.
Michael runs 24 laps and Isabel runs 15 laps.
Find the difference between the number of laps they run.

Michael — 24 laps
Isabel — 15 laps
?

24 − 15 = __9__

The difference is __9__ laps.

---

3 Find the difference.

Example

Find the difference between 40 and 17.

40
17
__23__

40 − 17 = __23__

The difference between 40 and 17 is __23__.

a Find the difference between 156 and 82.

156 − 82 = __74__

156
82
__74__

The difference between 156 and 82 is __74__.

b Find the difference between 800 and 785.

800 − 785 = __15__

800
785
__15__

The difference between 800 and 785 is __15__.

Practice 2 Simple subtraction within 10 000

1 Subtract. Use place value charts to help you.

Example

```
  3 8 1 7
-   7 0 5
─────────
  3 1 1 2
```

a
```
  9 3 4 9
- 5 1 3 8
─────────
  4 2 1 1
```

b
```
  7 3 5 2
- 4 3 2 1
─────────
  3 0 3 1
```

c
```
  5 4 9 3
- 3 2 9 1
─────────
  2 2 0 2
```

2 Subtract. Use place value charts to help you.

Example

5286 – 5000 = 286

5	2	8	6
5	0	0	0
2	8	6	

a 3646 – 2523 = 1123

3	6	4	6
2	5	2	3
1	1	2	3

---

6 The baker made 120 loaves on Monday.
She made 219 loaves on Tuesday.
How many more loaves did she make on Tuesday than on Monday?

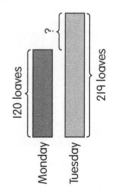

Monday 120 loaves
Tuesday 219 loaves ?

219 – 120 = 99
She made 99 more loaves on Tuesday than on Monday.

7 Miya's mum wants to buy a camera that costs £401.
She saves £315.
How much more does she need to save?

camera £401
savings £315 ?

£401 – £315 = £86
She needs to save £86 more.

Practice 3

Subtraction with regrouping in hundreds and thousands

1. Regroup the thousands and hundreds. Then subtract.

a)
```
   6 0 0 0
 -   8 0 0
   5 2 0 0
```

b)
```
   3 6 0 0
 - 1 7 0 0
   1 9 0 0
```

c)
```
   2 6 5 9
 - 1 9 4 3
     7 1 6
```

d)
```
   6 4 9 1
 - 3 5 7 0
   2 9 2 1
```

e)
```
   5 0 6 4
 - 4 7 3 2
     3 3 2
```

f)
```
   9 2 5 6
 - 3 6 2 5
   5 6 3 1
```

2. Subtract.

a) $8105 - 3672$
= 4433

b) $9346 - 7851$
= 1495

c) $2354 - 1690$
= 664

d) $3004 - 1681$
= 1323

e) $7059 - 673$
= 6386

f) $9007 - 984$
= 8023

b) $7249 - 249 =$ 7000

	7	2	4	9
−		2	4	9
	7	0	0	0

c) $9646 - 523 =$ 9123

	9	6	4	6
−		5	2	3
	9	1	2	3

d) $5546 - 23 =$ 5523

	5	5	4	6
−			2	3
	5	5	2	3

3. Use place value charts to help you answer these questions.

a Find the difference between 3497 and 2391.
3497 − 2391 = 1106

b Find the difference between 6974 and 813.
6974 − 813 = 6161

Practice 4

Subtraction with regrouping in ones, tens, hundreds and thousands

1 Follow the steps as you subtract.
Fill in the spaces.

Step 1:
$$\begin{array}{r} 8\ 2\ {}^6\!\!7\ {}^1\!0 \\ -\ 1\ 3\ 7\ 9 \\ \hline 1 \end{array}$$

Subtract the ones.
There are not enough ones.
Regroup the tens and ones.

7 tens 0 ones
= __6__ tens __10__ ones

Step 2:
$$\begin{array}{r} 8\ {}^1\!2\ {}^6\!7\ {}^1\!0 \\ -\ 1\ 3\ 7\ 9 \\ \hline 9\ 1 \end{array}$$

Subtract the tens.
There are not enough tens.
Regroup the hundreds and tens.

2 hundreds 6 tens
= __1__ hundred __16__ tens

Step 3:
$$\begin{array}{r} {}^7\!8\ {}^1\!2\ {}^6\!7\ {}^1\!0 \\ -\ 1\ 3\ 7\ 9 \\ \hline 8\ 9\ 1 \end{array}$$

Subtract the hundreds.
There are not enough hundreds.
Regroup the thousands and hundreds.

8 thousands 1 hundred
= __7__ thousands __11__ hundreds

Step 4:
$$\begin{array}{r} {}^7\!8\ {}^1\!2\ {}^6\!7\ {}^1\!0 \\ -\ 1\ 3\ 7\ 9 \\ \hline 6\ 8\ 9\ 1 \end{array}$$

Subtract the thousands.

---

3 What is the message at the bottom of the page?

Morse Code

A	B	C	D	E	F	G	H	I
·−	−···	−·−·	−··	·	··−·	−−·	····	··
J	K	L	M	N	O	P	Q	R
·−−−	−·−	·−··	−−	−·	−−−	·−−·	−−·−	·−·
S	T	U	V	W	X	Y	Z	
···	−	··−	···−	·−−	−··−	−·−−	−−··	

Write the answers in the boxes.
Each answer is represented by a symbol from Morse code.

a 8500 − 700 = [7800] −·−−

b 2600 − 900 = [1700] ·−

c 5120 − 600 = [4520] −−−

d 4789 − 1800 = [2989] ·

e 9363 − 5512 = [3851] −−·

f 3255 − 1731 = [1524] ·−·

g 3126 − 1724 = [1402] −

h 6043 − 3712 = [2331] ··−

Write the letters of Morse code that match the answers to find the message.

The message is

" Y   O   U ' R   E
7800 4520 2331   1524 2989

G   R   A   T !"
3851 1524 1700 1402

2 Follow the steps as you subtract.
Fill in the spaces.

Step 1:

$$\begin{array}{r} 4\ 3\ ^45\ ^17 \\ -\ 1\ 7\ 8\ 9 \\ \hline 8 \end{array}$$

Subtract the ones.
There are not enough ones.
Regroup the tens and ones.

5 tens 7 ones

= ___4___ tens ___17___ ones

Step 2:

$$\begin{array}{r} 4\ ^23\ ^45\ ^17 \\ -\ 1\ 7\ 8\ 9 \\ \hline 6\ 8 \end{array}$$

Subtract the tens.
There are not enough tens.
Regroup the hundreds and tens.

3 hundreds 4 tens

= ___2___ hundreds ___14___ tens

Step 3:

$$\begin{array}{r} ^34\ ^23\ ^15\ 7 \\ -\ 1\ 7\ 8\ 9 \\ \hline 5\ 6\ 8 \end{array}$$

Subtract the hundreds.
There are not enough hundreds.
Regroup the thousands and hundreds.

4 thousands 2 hundreds

= ___3___ thousands ___12___ hundreds

Step 4:

$$\begin{array}{r} ^34\ ^23\ ^15\ 7 \\ -\ 1\ 7\ 8\ 9 \\ \hline 2\ 5\ 6\ 8 \end{array}$$

Subtract the thousands.

3 Subtract the numbers. Regroup if you need to.

a)
$$\begin{array}{r} 5\ 1\ 6 \\ -\ 3\ 1\ 2 \\ \hline 2\ 0\ 4 \end{array}$$

b)
$$\begin{array}{r} 3\ 4\ 5 \\ -\ \ \ 6\ 9 \\ \hline 2\ 7\ 6 \end{array}$$

c)
$$\begin{array}{r} 8\ 7\ 3 \\ -\ 5\ 8\ 4 \\ \hline 2\ 8\ 9 \end{array}$$

d)
$$\begin{array}{r} 5\ 5\ 6 \\ -\ 2\ 8\ 7 \\ \hline 2\ 6\ 9 \end{array}$$

e)
$$\begin{array}{r} 1\ 4\ 3\ 6 \\ -\ \ \ 3\ 8\ 8 \\ \hline 1\ 0\ 4\ 8 \end{array}$$

f)
$$\begin{array}{r} 7\ 0\ 4 \\ -\ \ \ 2\ 9 \\ \hline 6\ 7\ 5 \end{array}$$

g)
$$\begin{array}{r} 9\ 1\ 9\ 1 \\ -\ 2\ 5\ 6\ 3 \\ \hline 6\ 6\ 2\ 8 \end{array}$$

h)
$$\begin{array}{r} 2\ 1\ 1\ 1 \\ -\ \ \ 1\ 9\ 7 \\ \hline 1\ 9\ 1\ 4 \end{array}$$

Colour the answers to find the path to the present.

4987	3876	1864
5533	1914	6628
1235	1048	9713
6753	289	276
204	269	438
276	1176	5763

675

Start here

54

4 Subtract to find the name of the largest planet in the Solar System.

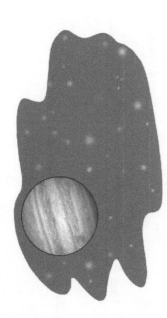

a $9585 - 8127 =$ **1458** **P**

b $6825 - 2975 =$ 3850 **I**

c $5824 - 3256 =$ 2568 **U**

d $2546 - 897 =$ 1649 **T**

e $4050 - 1888 =$ 2162 **E**

f $6010 - 799 =$ 5211 **R**

g $7901 - 607 =$ 7294 **J**

Write the letters that match the answers to find the name of the planet.

The planet is

J	U	P	I	T	E	R
7294	2568	1458	3850	1649	2162	5211

55

5 Subtract. Regroup if you need to.

a
```
   5 3 1 6
 -   7 8 5
 ─────────
   4 5 3 1
```

b
```
   9 3 4 2
 - 1 5 7 0
 ─────────
   7 7 7 2
```

c
```
   8 0 5 7
 - 2 7 6 3
 ─────────
   5 2 9 4
```

d
```
   6 5 0 7
 - 5 7 8 5
 ─────────
     7 2 2
```

e
```
   9 7 3 6
 - 8 8 7 5
 ─────────
     8 6 1
```

f
```
   3 0 5 6
 - 1 2 7 4
 ─────────
   1 7 8 2
```

Colour the spaces that contain the answers.

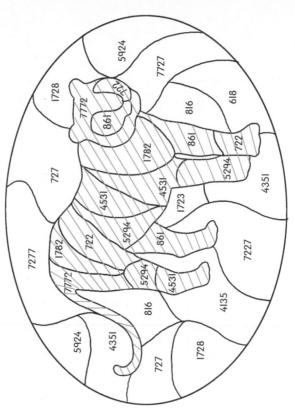

Can you tell which animal this is? A tiger

Practice 5

Subtraction with numbers that have zeros

1 Subtract.
Find Miya's favourite type of jam.

a
$$\begin{array}{r} 1000 \\ -\ 343 \\ \hline \end{array}$$
(p) 657

b
$$\begin{array}{r} 2006 \\ -\ 358 \\ \hline \end{array}$$
(e) 1648

c
$$\begin{array}{r} 6003 \\ -1437 \\ \hline \end{array}$$
(t) 4566

$$\begin{array}{r} 1000 \\ -\ 764 \\ \hline \end{array}$$
(y) 236

d
$$\begin{array}{r} 3000 \\ -2515 \\ \hline \end{array}$$
(r) 485

e
$$\begin{array}{r} 4000 \\ -1637 \\ \hline \end{array}$$
(a) 2363

f
$$\begin{array}{r} 8004 \\ -5476 \\ \hline \end{array}$$
(w) 2528

g
$$\begin{array}{r} 9001 \\ -5557 \\ \hline \end{array}$$
(s) 3444

h
$$\begin{array}{r} 7000 \\ -1999 \\ \hline \end{array}$$
(b) 5001

i
$$\begin{array}{r} 5003 \\ -2349 \\ \hline \end{array}$$
(z) 2654

Write the letters that match the answers.

Miya's favourite type of jam is:

s	t	r	a	w	b	e	r	y
3444	4566	485	2363	2528	5001	1648	485	236

---

6 Subtract.

a 3652 – 1821 = **(J)** 1831

b 7062 – 5102 = **(F)** 1960

c 7342 – 2502 = **(O)** 4840

d 8513 – 5662 = **(R)** 2851

e 6107 – 1725 = **(W)** 4382

f 7156 – 4327 = **(U)** 2829

g 2152 – 1648 = **(N)** 504

h 3475 – 2696 = **(E)** 779

i 5261 – 1385 = **(T)** 3876

j 9133 – 7269 = **(H)** 1864

k 3087 – 1779 = **(L)** 1308

l 7965 – 4978 = **(I)** 2987

Write the letters that match the answers to find the famous landmark.

E	I	F	F	E	L
779	2987	1960	1960	779	1308

T	H	E
3876	1864	779

T	O	W	E	R
3876	4840	4382	779	2851

Do you know where this landmark is? Paris

Challenging Practice

1 Use the numbers to complete the number sentence.

a The difference between the two numbers is 42.

 68   42   26   82

68 − 26 = 42

b The difference between the two numbers is 280.

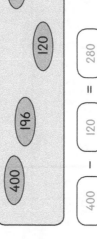 400   196   120   476

400 − 120 = 280
            196

2 Regroup the thousands and hundreds. Fill in the boxes.

a
```
  5 [6] 3 6
- 2  7  2 4
_____
  2  9  1 2
```

b
```
  8 [1] 7 5
- 3  4  4 3
_____
  4  7  3 2
```

---

2 Answer these questions.

Example

Tai has 1000 stickers.
Ella has 450 stickers.
How many more stickers does Tai have than Ella?

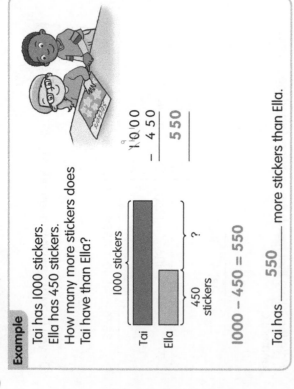

1000 stickers

Tai

Ella

450 stickers   ?

```
   9
 1̶0̶0̶0
- 4 5 0
_____
  5 5 0
```

1000 − 450 = 550

Tai has **550** more stickers than Ella.

Mr Taylor wants to give 4002 toys to the children's hospital.
He has 2157 toys.
How many more toys does he need?

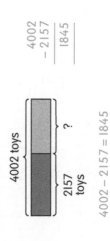

4002 toys

2157 toys   ?

```
  4002
- 2157
_____
  1845
```

4002 − 2157 = 1845

Mr Taylor needs **1845** more toys.

Problem Solving

1 Fill in the missing numbers.

a
```
   3 6 8 9
 - 2 ⑥ 9 5
   ___ 9 9 4
```

b
```
   7 3 2 ⑤
 - 3 8 7 9
   3 4 4 6
```

2 The difference between two numbers is 100.
One number is more than 90 but less than 100.
The other number is between 190 and 200.
What are two possible numbers?

Possible answers:
91 and 191
92 and 192
93 and 193
94 and 194
95 and 195
96 and 196
97 and 197
98 and 198
99 and 199

3 Use the digits below to make as many 4-digit numbers as you can.
Do not begin with '0'.

6, 5, 8, 2, 0

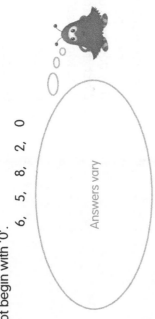

Answers vary

Subtract the smallest 4-digit number from the greatest number.

8652 − 2056 = 6596

4 Use the digits 0, 1, 4 and 7 to write a number greater than 5632.
Subtract 5632 from the number.

Answers vary

5 Use the digits 1, 6, 8 and 9 to write a number smaller than 3005.
Subtract the smaller number from 3005.

Answers vary

3 Jack and Peter play games at the fair.
The more games they win, the more points they collect.
They can swap their points for these prizes:

Pencil

30 points

Notebook

Note book

50 points

Coloured pencils

Coloured pencils

100 points

Pencil holder

200 points

Stationery set

300 points

Bag

500 points

After playing all the games, Jack has 215 points and
Peter has 78 points.
They add their points together.
Which three prizes can they swap their points for?
Write two possible answers.

a coloured pencils, notebook, pencil

b pencil holder, notebook, pencil

Unit 3: Subtraction of Numbers within 10 000

Unit 4: Solving Word Problems I: Addition and Subtraction

Medium-term plan

Week	Learning Objectives	Thinking Skills	Resources
6	**Word problems** Pupils will be able to: • apply addition concepts ('part-whole', 'adding on' and 'comparing') and subtraction concepts ('part-whole', 'taking away' and 'comparing') to solve two-step word problems • solve two-step word problems by using models that represent the problem situation • make up two-step word problems using given words and numbers in addition and subtraction *Let's Explore!* Pupils will be able to use addition and subtraction concepts (sum and difference) to investigate and discover a pattern from a series of calculations.	• Analysing and interpreting • Applying addition and subtraction concepts	• Pupil Textbook 3A, pp 56 to 60 • Practice Book 3A, pp 63 to 74 • Teacher's Guide 3A, pp 94 to 98
6	*Put On Your Thinking Caps!* Pupils will be able to draw diagrams or use 'guess and check' to solve a challenging problem.	• Making inferences Heuristic for problem solving: • Draw a diagram	• Pupil Textbook 3A, p 61 • Practice Book 3A, pp 75 to 78 • Teacher's Guide 3A, p 99
	Review 2 Revision 1		• Practice Book 3A, pp 79 to 88

Summative assessment opportunities

Assessment Book 3, Test 2, pp 7 to 12
For extension, Assessment Book 3, Challenging Problems 1, pp 13 to 14
Assessment Book 3, Check-up 1, pp 15 to 24

Solving Word Problems I: Addition and Subtraction

Learning objectives: Word problems

Pupils will be able to:

- apply addition concepts ('part-whole', 'adding on' and 'comparing') and subtraction concepts ('part-whole', 'taking away' and 'comparing') to solve two-step word problems

- solve two-step word problems by using models that represent the problem situation

- make up two-step word problems using given words and numbers in addition and subtraction

Key concept

Translating addition and subtraction concepts into models for solving two-step word problems

Teaching sequence

- Use the given model involving the 'comparing' (subtraction) and 'part-whole' concepts (addition) to explain how the two-step word problem is represented.

- To find the number of tickets Ella sold, the 'comparing' concept is used. To find the number of tickets Omar and Ella sold altogether, the 'part-whole' concept is used.

- **Note**: If necessary, help pupils to conceptualise the problem by highlighting some key words, e.g., 'fewer than' and using the comparing model. Say: *"Omar sold 3450 and Ella sold 1286 fewer tickets than Omar."*

Unit 4 | **Solving Word Problems I: Addition and Subtraction**

Let's Learn!

Word problems

1. Omar and Ella were selling raffle tickets. Omar sold 3450 tickets and Ella sold 1286 fewer tickets than Omar.
   a. How many tickets did Ella sell?
   b. How many tickets did they sell altogether?

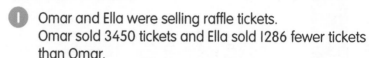

a. $3450 - 1286 = 2164$

   Ella sold 2164 raffle tickets.

b. $3450 + 2164 = 5614$

   Omar and Ella sold 5614 raffle tickets altogether.

 Home Maths Ask your child to make up three addition word problems using the following concepts: part-whole, adding on and comparing.

56

Thinking skills

- Analysing and interpretating
- Applying addition and subtraction concepts

2 A computer costs £1950.
The computer costs £250 less than the television.
How much do both items cost altogether?

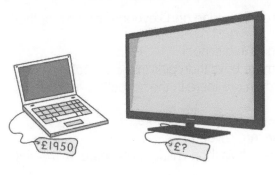

£1950   £?

Find out the cost of the television first!

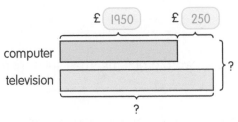

£ 1950   £ 250

computer

television

?

?

£ 1950 (+) £ 250 = £ 2200

The television costs £ 2200 .

£ 1950 (+) £ 2200 = £ 4150

Both items cost £ 4150 altogether.

Home Maths Ask your child to make up three subtraction word problems using the following concepts: part-whole, taking away and comparing.

57

Teaching sequence

2

- Work through this two-step word problem.
  Ask pupils to interpret the problem and to fill in the relevant information in the model given.
- This problem uses the 'comparing' and 'part-whole' concepts (addition).

Independent work

Practices I, 2 and 3 in Practice Book 3A, pp 63 to 74.

Additional activity

Ask pupils to create new word problems using the numbers in ④, so that they have to use the following operations to solve the problem:

(a) – and +

(b) – and –

(c) + and +

Teaching sequence

③ to **⑤**

- Ask pupils to solve these problems. Guide them to use the following strategy:

    I. Read and understand each problem.

    2. Highlight some key words and try to draw a model based on these key words.

    3. Draw the model and fill in all given data in the model.

    4. Interpret the model and write some statements to help solve the problem.

⑥

- Explain the example given. Ask pupils to work in pairs to:

    I. write three two-step word problems using the helping words given.

    2. solve each two-step word problem by translating question statements into a model, and then interpreting the model to solve the problem.

Unit 4 Solving Word Problems I: Addition and Subtraction

③ A piano costs £4770.
A keyboard costs £3250 less than the piano.

 a How much does the keyboard cost? £1520

 b How much do the piano and keyboard cost altogether? £6290

④ There are 720 girls in a school.
There are 250 more boys than girls in the school.
How many children are there in the school? 1690

⑤ On a ship there are 5099 passengers.
1825 passengers are children.
How many more adults than children are there on the ship? 1449

Activity

⑥ Make up some two-step word problems. Then solve them.

Example

Millie writes a two-step word problem using these words and numbers.

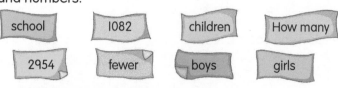

school | 1082 | children | How many

2954 | fewer | boys | girls

This is the word problem that Millie wrote:

There are 2954 children in a school.
1082 children are boys.
How many children are girls?
How many fewer boys than girls are there?

58

96   **Unit 4:** Solving Word Problems I: Addition and Subtraction

Activity

Here is the model to solve Millie's word problem on page 58:

```
        1082        ?
boys  [██████████]
                          } 2954
girls [            ]
              ?
```

2954 − 1082 = (1872)

(1872) children are girls.

(1872) − 1082 = (790)

There are (790) fewer boys than girls.

Write some two-step word problems using these words
and numbers.
Then solve them using the model. Answers vary

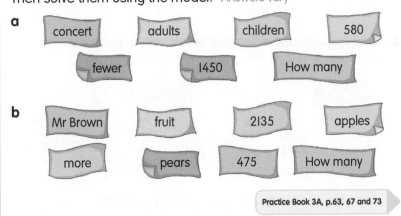

a

concert   adults   children   580

fewer   1450   How many

b

Mr Brown   fruit   2135   apples

more   pears   475   How many

Practice Book 3A, p.63, 67 and 73

Home
Maths
Find opportunities to ask your child to solve word problems when you
go shopping or on a journey. For example, there are 36 men and 12
women on the bus. How many people are on the bus?

59

Objective of activity

Pupils will be able to use addition and subtraction concepts (sum and difference) to investigate and discover a pattern from a series of calculations.

Teaching sequence

7 *Let's Explore!*

- Carry out the procedure in this activity. Encourage pupils to look for the pattern: when we add the sum and the difference of two numbers, the total is always twice the greater number.

- Encourage pupils to think of two other numbers to confirm the result.

Let's Explore!

7

1 Think of a pair of numbers.

> 9 and 4

> 12 and 7

2 Find the sum and difference of the pair of numbers.

> 9 + 4 = 13
> 9 – 4 = 5

> 12 + 7 = 19
> 12 – 7 = 5

sum

difference

3 Add the sum and difference of the pair of numbers. Compare this with the greater number in the pair.

> 13 + 5 = 18

> 19 + 5 = 24

> Compare 18 and 9.

> Compare 24 and 12.

4 Repeat steps **1** to **3** with other pairs of numbers.

5 Can you see a pattern?

60

Solving Word Problems I: Addition and Subtraction **Unit 4**

Put On Your Thinking Caps!

8 The farmer has eight mystery animals in his barn.
Some have 2 legs and some have 4 legs.
The mystery animals have 20 legs altogether.
How many mystery animals with 4 legs are there?
If there were four kinds of animals on the farm, name what they could be.

Draw a circle for every mystery animal. Start by drawing 2 legs on each animal.

Remember to draw 20 legs altogether.

There are (two) animals with 4 legs.

The mystery animals could be (horse), (cow), (ducks) and (chickens).

Practice Book 3A, p.75   Practice Book 3A, p.78

61

Teaching sequence

8 *Put On Your Thinking Caps!*

- This section introduces a non-routine problem. The strategy for solving the problem is either to use the 'drawing' strategy or a multi-step approach.

- Ensure that pupils are aware of the two conditions that must be fulfilled in order to solve the problem:
  1) There are 8 animals altogether.
  2) The animals have 20 legs altogether.

- Ask pupils to draw legs on to 8 animals. The strategy is to first give 2 legs to each animal. Then to add the remaining number of legs. The remaining number of legs must be for the four-legged animals. There are 2 four-legged animals.

- Ask pupils similar problems such as:
  "There are 10 rabbits and an unknown number of ducks. The farmer counted the number of legs and found that there are 30 legs altogether. How many rabbits are there?"

Unit 4

Solving Word Problems I: Addition and Subtraction

Date: _____

Practice I Word problems

Read these word problems. Fill in the spaces to solve them.

1. A Year 3 class raises £4250 for charity. A Year 4 class raises £825 more than the Year 3 class.

   a How much money does the Year 4 class raise?

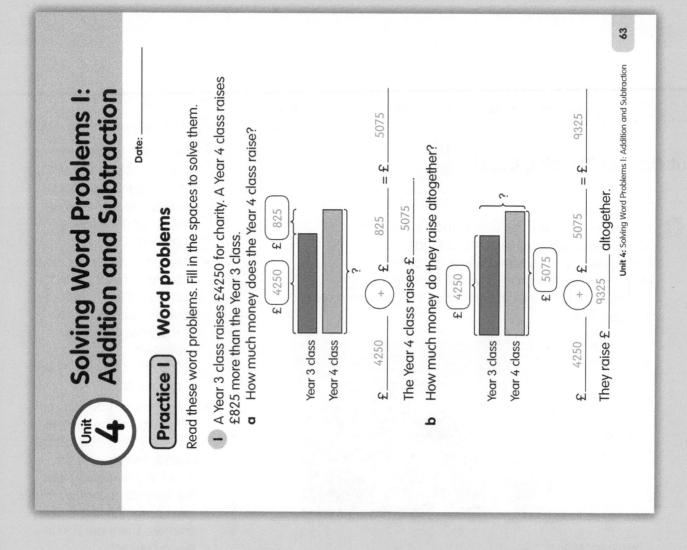

   | Year 3 class | £ 4250 |
   | Year 4 class | £ 825 |

   £ __4250__ + £ __825__ = £ __5075__

   The Year 4 class raises £ __5075__ .

   b How much money do they raise altogether?

   | Year 3 class | £ 4250 |
   | Year 4 class | £ 5075 |

   £ __4250__ + £ __5075__ = £ __9325__

   They raise £ __9325__ altogether.

3 There are 4320 books and magazines in a shop.
There are 2169 books.
The rest are magazines.

a How many magazines are there?

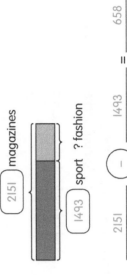

4320   –   2169   =   2151

There are ___2151___ magazines.

b There are 1493 sport magazines and the rest are
fashion magazines.
How many fashion magazines are there?

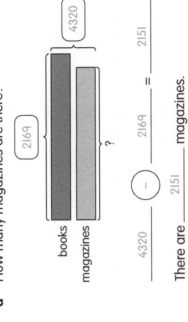

2151   –   1493   =   658

There are ___658___ fashion magazines.

---

2 Peter has 487 coins.
Miya has 175 fewer coins than Peter.

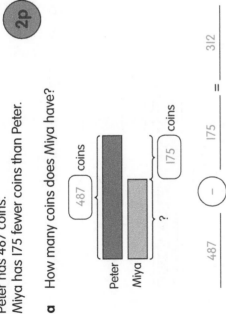

a How many coins does Miya have?

487   –   175   =   312

Miya has ___312___ coins.

b How many coins do they have altogether?

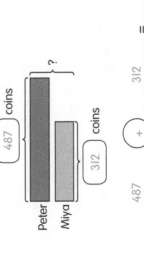

487   +   312   =   799

They have ___799___ coins altogether.

Practice 2 Word problems

Draw models and solve these word problems.
Fill in the circles and spaces.

1 Ella has 1458 football stickers.
She has 396 fewer football stickers than Jack.

a How many football stickers does Jack have?

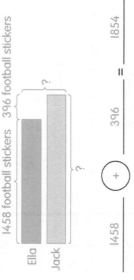

Ella
Jack
1458 football stickers   396 football stickers
?

1458 (+) 396 = 1854

Jack has __1854__ football stickers.

b How many football stickers do they have altogether?

1458 (+) 1854 = 3312

They have __3312__ football stickers altogether.

---

4 Farha's skipping rope is 1452 cm long.
Omar's skipping rope is 379 cm longer than Farha's.

a How long is Omar's skipping rope?

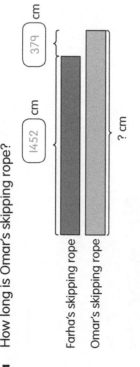

Farha's skipping rope   1452 cm   379 cm
Omar's skipping rope   ? cm

1452 (+) 379 = 1831

Omar's skipping rope is __1831__ cm long.

b Omar cuts 645 cm off his skipping rope.
How long is his skipping rope now?

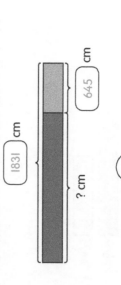

1831 cm   645 cm   ? cm

1831 (−) 645 = 1186

Omar's skipping rope is now __1186__ cm long.

2 There are 1287 women at a tennis match.
There are 879 fewer men at the match.

a How many men are there?

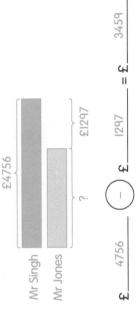

1287 (−) 879 = 408

There are ___408___ men.

b How many people are there altogether?

1287 (+) 408 = 1695

There are ___1695___ people altogether.

---

3 Mr Singh has £4756.
Mr Jones has £1297 less than Mr Singh.

a How much does Mr Jones have?

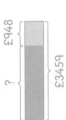

£4756 (−) £1297 = £3459

Mr Jones has £ ___3459___

b How much will Mr Jones have left if he spends £948?

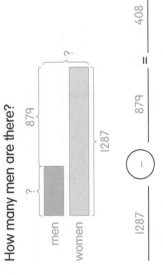

£3459 (−) £948 = £2511

Mr Jones will have £ ___2511___ left if he spends £948.

4 The Fun Stuff factory makes 1793 toys.
It makes 157 fewer toys than the Cool Toys factory.

a How many toys does the Cool Toys factory make?

Fun Stuff — 1793 toys

Cool Toys — 157 toys — ?

1793 $+$ 157 $=$ 1950

The Cool Toys factory makes ___1950___ toys.

b If the Cool Toys factory sells 1698 toys, how many toys will it have left?

1698 toys

1950 toys

?

1950 $-$ 1698 $=$ 252

It will have ___252___ toys left.

5 The headteacher printed 635 newsletters on Monday.
She printed 96 fewer newsletters on Wednesday.

a How many newsletters did she print on Wednesday?
b How many newsletters did she print altogether?

a

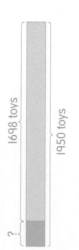

Monday — 635 newsletters — ?

Wednesday — 96 newsletters

$635 - 96 = 539$
She printed 539 newsletters on Wednesday.

b $635 + 539 = 1174$
She printed 1174 newsletters altogether.

Practice 3   Word problems

Draw models to help you solve these word problems.

1 Hardeep mixes 620 litres of water with 180 litres of lemon squash to make drinks for a school fair.
He adds another 145 litres of water to the mixture.
How much more water than squash does he use for the drinks?

squash   180 litres   ?

water   620 litres   145 litres

620 + 145 = 765
765 litres of water is used.

765 − 180 = 585
585 litres more water than squash is used for the drinks.

First find the total amount of water used.

---

6 Alisha's school raises £3756 for charity.
Ben's school raises £455 more than Alisha's school.

a How much money does Ben's school raise?

b How much money do the schools raise altogether?

a

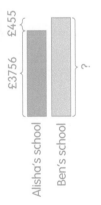

Alisha's school   £3756   £455

Ben's school   ?

3756 + 455 = 4211
Ben's school raises £4211.

b

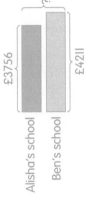

Alisha's school   £3756

Ben's school   £4211   ?

3756 + 4211 = 7967
The schools raises £7967 altogether.

Page 74

2 A shopkeeper sells 3500 g of flour to Ava.
He sells 500 g less flour to Mark than to Ava.
He sells 750 g less flour to Tom than to Mark.
How much flour does he sell to Tom?

Ava — 3500 g

Mark — 500 g

Tom — 750 g

3500 − 500 = 3000
The shopkeeper sells 3000 g of flour to Mark.

3000 − 750 = 2250
The shopkeeper sells 2250 g of flour to Tom.

Page 75

Date: _____

Challenging Practice

1 Tai has been collecting football stickers since he was 5 years old.
He has not thrown away any of his football stickers.
He is now 7 years old.
He collected 201 stickers last year.
He has collected 125 stickers this year.
He has 589 stickers altogether now.

a How many stickers did he have in total at the end of last year?

b How many stickers did he have when he was 5 years old?

a 589 − 125 = 464
He had 464 stickers in total at the end of last year.

b 464 − 201 = 263
He had 263 stickers when he was 5 years old.

2 Farha, Jack and Omar collect money for charity after a sponsored swim.
Farha collects £350.
Jack collects £20 more than Farha.
Omar collects the same amount as the total amount that Farha and Jack collect.
How much do the three children collect in total?

350 + 20 = 370
Jack collects £370.

350 + 370 + 350 + 370 = 1440
The three children collect £1440 in total.

Now you try it!

Word problem

Model

Solution

Answers vary

Maths Journal

Date: _____

Isabel saves £2960.
Nick saves £2662.

Isabel saves £298 more than Nick.
Nick saves £298 less than Isabel.
Isabel and Nick save £5622 altogether.

How much does Isabel save?
How much does Nick save?
How much more does Isabel save than Nick?
How much less does Nick save than Isabel?
How much do they save altogether?

1 Make a 1-step word problem. Use the sentences in the bubbles.
Draw a model for your word problem. Then solve it.

Example

Word problem

Isabel saves £2960.
Nick saves £298 less than Isabel.
How much does Nick save?

Model

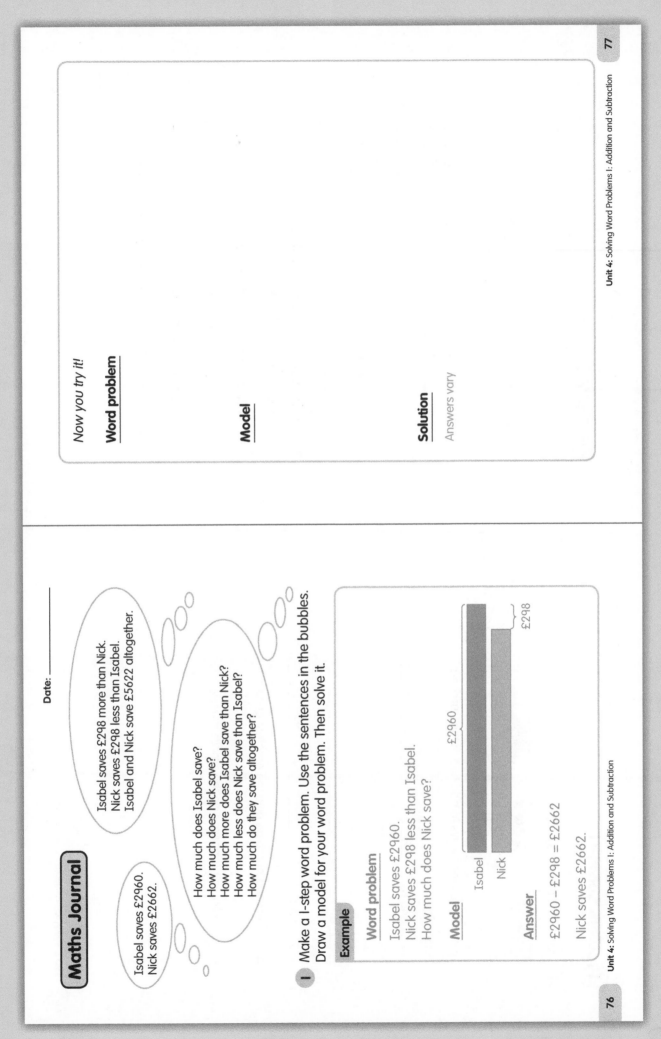

Answer

£2960 − £298 = £2662

Nick saves £2662.

Review 2

Date: _____

1 The difference between 273 and 1000 is __727__.

2 Subtract.

a
```
   8 7 5 4
 -   5 3 1
 ─────────
   8 2 2 3
```

b
```
   8 6 1 5
 - 2 7 0 4
 ─────────
   5 9 1 1
```

c
```
   2 5 6 1
 -   6 8 4
 ─────────
   1 8 7 7
```

d
```
   5 0 1 0
 - 3 6 8 5
 ─────────
   1 3 2 5
```

3 Fill in the boxes. Do not begin with '0'.

a (5) (0) (1) (6)

Use the digits above to make:

the greatest 4-digit number. __6510__

the smallest 4-digit number. __1056__

b Find the difference between the two numbers in **a**. __5454__

Problem Solving

Date: _____

1 Look at the numbers below.

318	456	195
A	B	C

Think of two other ways to add two of the numbers.

Example

A and B: __318__ + __456__ = __774__

__B__ and __C__ : __456__ + __195__ = 651

__A__ and __C__ : __318__ + __195__ = 513

a Which two numbers give the greatest answer? __A and B__

b Which two numbers give the smallest answer? __A and C__

Solve these word problems.
Draw models to help you.

6 A sponsored run raises £2500 for charity.
A car boot sale raises £1957 for the same charity.
How much money is raised for the charity altogether?

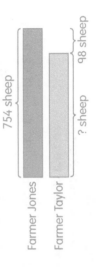

£2500   £1957

£?

£2500 + £1957 = £4457
£4457 is raised for the charity altogether.

7 Farmer Jones has 754 sheep on his farm.
He has 98 more sheep than Farmer Taylor.
How many sheep does Farmer Taylor have?

754 sheep

Farmer Jones

Farmer Taylor

? sheep   98 sheep

754 − 98 = 656
Farmer Taylor has 656 sheep.

---

4 Fill in the missing number.

```
  6 0 0 0
- 4 ⬚ 1 3
  ─────────
  1 9 8 7
```

5 Daniel throws two darts at the dartboard below.

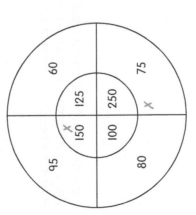

95   60   125   150

100   250

80   75   ✗

Which numbers do the darts land on?
Clue: The difference between the two numbers is 75.
Put crosses (✗) on the dartboard.

Answers Unit 4: Solving Word Problems I: Addition and Subtraction   109

Revision I

Date: _____

Section A
Choose the correct answer.
Write its letter in the box.

1 In the number 6592, the digit 5 is in the _____ place.

  a ones   **b** tens
  c hundreds   **d** thousands

         c

2 Which number is 1000 more than 1629?

  a 629   **b** 1619
  c 1729   **d** 2629

         d

3 Add 5143 and 1625.

  a 4518   **b** 6768
  c 6868   **d** 7768

         b

4 Subtract 2511 from 5876.

  a 1635   **b** 3365
  c 5625   **d** 8387

         b

5 Complete the number pattern.

  5273,   6263,   7253,   _____

  a 4263   **b** 8243
  c 8273   **d** 8364

         b

---

8 Mrs Brown has £5475.
Mr Brown has £1496 less than Mrs Brown.
  a How much does Mr Brown have?
  b How much do they have altogether?

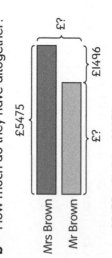

a   £5475 − £1496 = £3979
    Mr Brown has £3979.

b   £5475 + £3979 = £9454
    They have £9454 altogether.

9 There are 659 children at a football match.
There are 3615 more adults than children.
How many people are there at the football match?

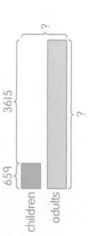

659 + 3615 = 4274
There are 4274 adults at the football match.

659 + 4274 = 4933
There are 4933 people at the football match.

6 6 thousands and 4 hundreds makes _____.

a   64   b   604

c   640   d   6400

> d

7 300 more than 459 is _____.

a   462   b   489

c   759   d   3459

> c

8 Add 685 to 2469.

a   1784   b   3154

c   9319   d   10000

> b

9 What is the missing digit in the box?

```
   5 □ 2 9
 + 3 6 9 4
 ---------
   8 9 2 3
```

a   1   b   2

c   3   d   5

> b

10 Which of these pairs has a difference of 500?

a   2659 and 2259

b   3036 and 3545

c   5489 and 489

d   8426 and 8926

> d

Section B

Read the questions and fill in the answers.

11 Write 7512 in words.

seven thousand, five hundred and twelve

12 Millie has two numbers: 1486 and 512.
Find the sum of the two numbers.

1998

13 Find the sum of 4750 and 3800.

8550

14 Omar has two cards.

6841   1057

What is the difference between the numbers on the cards?

5784

15 Find the difference between 3094 and 1258.

1836

16 Arrange the numbers in order. Begin with the smallest.

3715, 7315, 3571, 3751

3571 , 3715 , 3751 , 7315

17 Add.

```
  3 8 6 5
+ 2 9 5 7
```
6822

18 Subtract 2859 from 5000.

2141

19 The sum of two numbers is 15.
One of the numbers is 3 less than the other.
Find these two numbers from the box below.

12, 6, 18, 7, 8, 9

6, 9

20 Look at the number pattern.

3272, 4482, 5692

What is added to each number to get the next number?

1210

Section C
Read the questions.
Show your workings in the spaces provided.

21 Mr Davies saves £2651.
Mrs Davies saves £2150 more than Mr Davies.
How much do they save altogether?

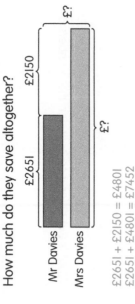

£2651 + £2150 = £4801
£2651 + £4801 = £7452

Mrs Davies saves £ 4801 .

They save £ 7452 altogether.

22 Ruby sells 3860 raffle tickets at a school fair.
She sells 750 fewer raffle tickets than Peter.
Millie sells 315 fewer raffle tickets than Peter.
How many raffle tickets does Millie sell?

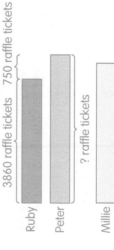

3860 + 750 = 4610
Peter sells 4610 raffle tickets.
4610 – 315 = 4295
Millie sells 4295 raffle tickets.

23 The supermarket donates £3700 to Charity A.
It donates £450 less to Charity B.
a How much does the supermarket donate to Charity B?
b How much does the supermarket donate altogether?

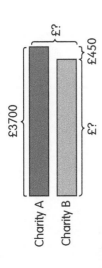

£3700

£?

Charity A

Charity B

£? £450

a £3700 − £450 = £3250
The supermarket donates £3250 to Charity B.

b £3700 + £3250 = £6950
The supermarket donates £6950 altogether.

24 There are 8652 books in a library.
There are 4623 fiction books and the rest are non-fiction books.
How many more fiction books than non-fiction books are there?

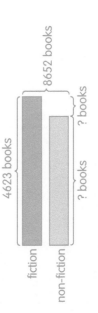

4623 books

fiction

non-fiction

8652 books

? books

? books

8652 − 4623 = 4029
There are 4029 non-fiction books.

4623 − 4029 = 594
There are 594 more fiction books than non-fiction books.

Unit 5: Multiplying by 6, 7, 8 and 9

Medium-term plan

Week	Learning Objectives	Thinking Skills	Resources
1	**(1) Multiplying by 6: skip-counting** Pupils will be able to: • recall multiplication concepts in groups of 6 and multiplying by 6 • use the 'skip-count in sixes' strategy to find the six times table facts • write multiplication sentences involving 6, given different problem situations • commit the six times table facts to memory	• Associating • Relating • Identifying relationships • Recalling • Applying multiplication facts	• Pupil Textbook 3A, pp 62 to 64 • Practice Book 3B, pp 5 to 6 • Teacher's Guide 3A, pp 118 to 120
1	**(2) Multiplying by 7: skip-counting** Pupils will be able to: • recall multiplication concept in groups of 7 and multiplying by 7 • use the 'skip-count in sevens' strategy to find the seven times table facts • write multiplication sentences involving 7, given different problem situations • commit the seven times table facts to memory	• Associating • Relating • Identifying relationships	• Pupil Textbook 3A, pp 65 to 66 • Practice Book 3B, pp 7 to 8 • Teacher's Guide 3A, pp 121 to 122

Unit 5: Multiplying by 6, 7, 8 and 9

Week	Learning Objectives	Thinking Skills	Resources
1	**(3) Multiplying by 8: skip-counting** Pupils will be able to: • recall multiplication concepts in groups of 8 and multiplying by 8 • use the 'skip-count in eights' strategy to find the eight times table facts • write multiplication sentences involving 8, given different problem situations • commit the eight times table facts to memory	• Associating • Relating • Identifying relationships	• Pupil Textbook 3A, pp 67 to 68 • Practice Book 3B, pp 9 to 10 • Teacher's Guide 3A, pp 123 to 124
1	**(4) Multiplying by 9** Pupils will be able to: • recall multiplication concepts in groups of 9 and multiplying by 9 • use the 'finger counting' method to find the nine times table facts • write multiplication sentences involving 9, given different problem situations • commit the nine times table facts to memory	• Associating • Relating • Identifying relationships	• Pupil Textbook 3A, pp 69 to 71 • Practice Book 3B, pp 11 to 12 • Teacher's Guide 3A, pp 125 to 127

Unit 5: Multiplying by 6, 7, 8 and 9

Week	Learning Objectives	Thinking Skills	Resources

2	**(5) Short cut method for multiplying by 6, 7, 8 and 9**
	
	Pupils will be able to:
	• use the 'connecting fact' strategy starting from 5 × 6 to find more difficult facts of 6
	• use the 'connecting fact' strategy starting from 5 × 7 to find more difficult facts of 7
	• use the 'connecting fact' strategy starting from 5 × 8 to find more difficult facts of 8
	• use the 'connecting fact' strategy starting from 5 × 9 to find more difficult facts of 9
	
	Let's Explore!
	
	Pupils will be able to:
	• discover the pattern of multiples of 5:
	  (a) whenever an even number is multiplied by 5, it has 0 as its ones digit
	  (b) whenever an odd number is multiplied by 5, it has 5 as its ones digit
		• Associating
		• Relating
		• Identifying relationships
			• Pupil Textbook 3A, pp 72 to 73
			• Practice Book 3B, pp 13 to 16
			• Teacher's Guide 3A, pp 128 to 129

Unit 5: Multiplying by 6, 7, 8 and 9

Week	Learning Objectives	Thinking Skills	Resources
2	**(6) Division: finding the number of items in each group** Pupils will be able to: • recall division concepts in finding the number of items in each group • find division facts by recalling multiplication facts • relate division and multiplication facts • write division facts from given multiplication facts • write multiplication facts from given division facts • write division sentences involving 6, 7, 8 or 9, given different problem situations	• Associating • Relating • Identifying relationships	• Pupil Textbook 3A, pp 74 to 75 • Practice Book 3B, pp 17 to 18 • Teacher's Guide 3A, pp 130 to 131
2	**(7) Division: making equal groups** Pupils will be able to: • recall division concepts in finding the number of groups • find division facts by recalling multiplication facts • relate division and multiplication facts • write division facts from given multiplication facts • write multiplication facts from given division facts • write division sentences involving 6, 7, 8 or 9, given different problem situations	• Associating • Relating • Identifying relationships	• Pupil Textbook 3A, pp 76 to 77 • Practice Book 3B, pp 19 to 20 • Teacher's Guide 3A, pp 132 to 133
2	*Put On Your Thinking Caps!* Pupils will be able to apply multiplication and division facts to find the numbers.	• Associating • Relating • Identifying relationships	• Pupil Textbook 3A, p 78 • Practice Book 3B, pp 21 to 22 • Teacher's Guide 3A, p 134

Multiplying by 6, 7, 8 and 9

Learning objectives:
Multiplying by 6:
skip-counting

Pupils will be able to:

- recall multiplication concepts in groups of 6 and multiplying by 6
- use the 'skip-count in sixes' strategy to find the six times table facts

- write multiplication sentences involving 6, given different problem situations
- commit the six times table facts to memory

Key concepts

- The 'group and item' concept is used for the multiplication facts of 6.
- Repeated addition is used for multiplication.

Teaching sequence

- Recall and explain the concept of multiplication as groups of items, or repeated addition.
- Emphasise the convention that the first factor refers to the number of groups and the second factor to the number of items in each group.
- Relate the convention above to the example of 4 ladybirds with 6 legs each. Write the statement '4 × 6 = 24' to show the relationship.
- Demonstrate the 'skip-counting' strategy using fingers to help pupils recall the multiplication facts.
- In this strategy, one finger represents 6 items and two fingers represent 12 items (i.e., 6 + 6 = 12).
- Show the whole list of multiplication facts of 6.
- Ask pupils to recite the sequence of numbers while showing the corresponding fingers. This exercise should be repeated until they are proficient in the 6 times table.

Unit 5 **Multiplying by 6, 7, 8 and 9**

Let's Learn!

Multiplying by 6: skip-counting

 4 × 6 = 24

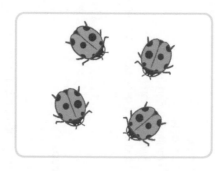

Each ladybird has 6 legs.

6 + 6 + 6 + 6 = 4 × 6

Count in sixes: 6, 12, 18, 24.

6 12 18 24

The ladybirds have 24 legs altogether.

62

Thinking skills

- Associating
- Relating
- Identifying relationships
- Recalling
- Applying multiplication facts

Additional activity

Ask pupils to work in pairs or in groups of six. Use concrete representations to show groups of six.

Ask the class to count in sixes. '6, 12, 18, 24, 30, 36, 42, 48, 54, 60'

Pupils should look for a number pattern in the ones digits of the multiples of 6: 6, 2, 8, 4, 0, 6, 2, 8, 4, 0 ...

What you will need

- Number-train cut-outs (see Photocopy master 7 on page 267)
- Dice

Multiplying by 6, 7, 8 and 9 **Unit 5**

2 There are 3 bees.
Each bee has 6 legs.
How many legs do the bees have altogether?

Count in sixes: 6, 12 , 18 .

$6 + 6 + 6$
$= 3 \times 6$

$3 \times 6 = 18$

The bees have 18 legs altogether.

Game

3 **Colour the number train!**

How to play:
Each player makes a number train like this on a piece of paper.

Coach A: 8 12 18 Coach B: 28 36 54 Coach C: 16 42 30

Players: 2 to 6
You will need:
- a number train for each player
- Dice A with numbers 1/2, 3/4, 5/6, 6/7, 7/8, 8/9
- Dice B with numbers 2, 4 and 6 repeated two times

1 Player 1 rolls Dice A and chooses a number on the dice. For example, they get the numbers 1/2. They choose 2.

2 Player 1 then rolls Dice B to get the next number. For example, they get the number 6. They multiply the two numbers: $6 \times 2 = 12$ The other players check the answer.

63

Teaching sequence

2

- Ask pupils to read the question and relate the context to multiplication. Invite volunteers to explain how to apply the concept to the problem.
- Ask pupils to use the 'skip-counting' strategy to find the answer.

3 *Game*

- The objective of this activity is for pupils to practise applying the 2, 4 and 6 multiplication facts.
- Make copies of the cut-out of a number-train.
- Prepare dice A by sticking the numbers 1/2, 3/4, 5/6, 6/7, 7/8 and 8/9 on the faces of a dice.
- Prepare dice B by sticking the numbers 2, 4 and 6 twice on the faces of a dice.
- Ask pupils to play the game in groups of 4 to 6. Give each group dice A and dice B, and each player a cut-out of a number train.
- Ask pupils to play the game by following the instructions in the textbook.
- The first pupil to shade the train is the winner.

Independent work

Practice I in Practice Book 3B,
pp 5 to 6.

Teaching sequence

4 and **5**

- Ask pupils to practise using the multiplication facts of 6 using the 'skip-counting' strategy.
- Pupils should check each other's answers.

Game

3 If the correct answer is on Coach A of the number train, Player I colours the answer in.

4 Take turns to play. Each player must colour the numbers on Coach A of the number train before going on to the next coach. Each player gets a bonus roll after colouring a whole coach.

The first person to colour all the numbers on all three coaches wins!

4 Answer these questions.

a 6, 12, 18, (24), (30), (36)

b 24, 30, 36, (42), (48), (54)

c 6 × 5 30   d 6 × 6 36

e 7 × 6 42   f 8 × 6 48

g 6 × 9 54   h 6 × 10 60

5 6 times table

I × 6 = 6	2 × 6 = 12	3 × 6 = 18	4 × 6 = 24	5 × 6 = 30
6 × 6 = 36	7 × 6 = 42	8 × 6 = 48	9 × 6 = 54	10 × 6 = 60

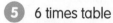

Home Maths Play the number train game with your child. You can replace the numbers on the train with any of the following: 2, 4, 6, 10, 20, 24, 32 and 48.

64

Practice Book 3B, p.5

Learning objectives: Multiplying by 7: skip-counting

Pupils will be able to:

- recall multiplication concepts in groups of 7 and multiplying by 7
- use the 'skip-count in sevens' strategy to find the seven times table facts
- write multiplication sentences involving 7, given different problem situations
- commit the seven times table facts to memory

Key concepts

- The 'group and item' concept is used for the multiplication facts of 7.
- Repeated addition is used for multiplication.

Thinking skills

- Associating
- Relating
- Identifying relationships

Let's Learn!

Multiplying by 7: skip-counting

1 5 × 7 = 35

Each group has 7 kittens.

Count in sevens: 7, 14, 21, 28, 35.

7 14 21 28 35

65

Teaching sequence

1

- Explain the concept of multiplication. Emphasise the convention that one of the factors refers to the number of groups and the other factor to the number of items in each group.
- Relate the convention above to the example of 5 groups of kittens with 7 kittens in each group. Write the statement '5 × 7 = 35' to show the relationship.
- Explain and show the 'skip-counting' strategy using finger representation to help pupils recall the multiplication facts.
- In this strategy, one finger represents 7 items and two fingers represent 14 items (i.e., 7 + 7 = 14).
- Show the whole list of multiplication facts of 7.
- Ask pupils to recite the sequence of numbers while showing the corresponding fingers. This exercise should be repeated until they are proficient in the 7 times table. (7, 14, 21, 28, 35, 42, 49, 56, 63, 70)

Additional activity

Ask pupils to look at the ones digits of the multiples of 7:

7, 1**4**, 2**1**, 2**8**, 3**5**
4**2**, 4**9**, 5**6**, 6**3**, **70**
7**7**, 8**4** ...

Help them to see that the digits make a repeating pattern.

Teaching sequence

- Ask pupils to read the question and relate the context to multiplication. Invite volunteers to explain how to apply the concept to the problem.
- Ask pupils to use the 'skip-counting' strategy to find the answer.

3 and **4**

- Ask pupils to work in small groups or in pairs to practise the 'skip-counting' strategy and to find multiplication facts of 7.

Unit 5 Multiplying by 6, 7, 8 and 9

2 There are 7 pea pods.
Each pod has 7 peas.
How many peas are there altogether?

Count in sevens:
7, 14, 21, 28 , 35 , 42 , 49

7 × 7 = 49

There are 49 peas altogether.

3 Answer these questions.

a   7, 14, 21, 28 , 35 , 42

b   28, 35, 42, 49 , 56 , 63

c   4 × 7 28   d   7 × 5 35

e   7 × 6 42   f   8 × 7 56

g   9 × 7 63   h   10 × 7 70

4 7 times table

| 1 × 7 = 7 | 2 × 7 = 14 | 3 × 7 = 21 | 4 × 7 = 28 | 5 × 7 = 35 |
| 6 × 7 = 42 | 7 × 7 = 49 | 8 × 7 = 56 | 9 × 7 = 63 | 10 × 7 = 70 |

Practice Book 3B, p.7

66

Learning objectives: Multiplying by 8: skip-counting

Pupils will be able to:

- recall multiplication concepts in groups of 8 and multiplying by 8
- use the 'skip-count in eights' strategy to find the eight times table facts
- write multiplication sentences involving 8, given different problem situations
- commit the eight times table facts to memory

Key concepts

- The 'group and item' concept is used for the multiplication facts of 8.
- Repeated addition is used for multiplication.

Thinking skills

- Associating
- Relating
- Identifying relationships

Let's Learn!

Multiplying by 8: skip-counting

① 3 × 8 = 24

 Each octopus has 8 legs.

Count in eights: 8, 16, 24.

 8   **16**   **24**

Three octopuses have 24 legs altogether.

② Dan has 5 tiles.
Each tile has 8 sides.
How many sides do the tiles have altogether?

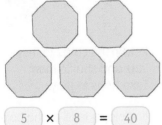

Count in eights: 8, 16, 24, 32, 40.

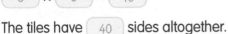
[5] × [8] = [40]

The tiles have [40] sides altogether.

67

Teaching sequence

①

- Ask pupils to recall multiplication as groups of items.
- Relate the concept above to the example of 3 octopuses with 8 legs each.
  Write '3 × 8 = 24' to show the relationship.
- Show the 'skip-counting' strategy using fingers to help pupils recall the multiplication facts.
- In this strategy, one finger represents 8 items and two fingers represent 16 items (i.e., 8 + 8 = 16).
- List the multiplication facts of 8. (8, 16, 24, 32, 40, 48, 56, 64, 72, 80)
- Pupils should recite the sequence of numbers while showing the corresponding fingers.

②

- Ask pupils to read the question and relate it to multiplication. Invite volunteers to explain how to apply the concept to the problem.
- Ask pupils to use the 'skip-counting' strategy to find the answer.

Thinking skills
- Recalling
- Applying multiplication facts

What you will need
- Set A: cards with numbers from 6 to 8. (Photocopy master 8)
- Set B: cards with numbers from 1 to 9. (Photocopy master 8)
- Worksheets (see Photocopy master 8 on pages 268 and 269)

Independent work
Practice 3 in Practice Book 3B, pp 9 to 10.

Additional activity
Ask pupils to look at the ones digits of the multiples of 8.

8, 1**6**, 2**4**, 3**2**, 4**0**
4**8**, 5**6**, 6**4**, 7**2**, 8**0**
8**8**, 9**6** ...

Help them see that the digits make a pattern of even numbers in descending order, beginning with 8: 8, 6, 4, 2, 0, 8, 6, 4, 2, 0 ...

Teaching sequence

3 to **4**

- Ask pupils to work in small groups or in pairs to practise the 'skip-counting' strategy and find multiplication facts of 8.

5 *Game*

- Make copies of the worksheet as shown on p 68.
- Prepare a pack of cards A with numbers from 6 to 8.
- Prepare a pack of cards B with numbers 1 to 9.
- Ask pupils to play the game in groups. Give each group a pack of cards A and a pack of cards B. Give each player a worksheet.
- Follow the steps on p 68.
- The first pupil to fill all the boxes correctly is the winner.

Unit 5 Multiplying by 6, 7, 8 and 9

3 Answer these questions.

a 8, 16, 24, (32), (40), (48)

b 32, 40, 48, (56), (64), (72)

c 6 × 8 48   d 7 × 8 56   e 8 × 9 72   f 8 × 10 80

4 8 times table

| 1 × 8 = 8 | 2 × 8 = 16 | 3 × 8 = 24 | 4 × 8 = 32 | 5 × 8 = 40 |
| 6 × 8 = 48 | 7 × 8 = 56 | 8 × 8 = 64 | 9 × 8 = 72 | 10 × 8 = 80 |

Game

5 **Double cards!**

How to play:

Each player is given a worksheet.

×	1	2	3	4	5	6	7	8	9
8									
7									
6									

Players: 2 to 6
You will need:
- a worksheet for each player
- Set A: cards with numbers from 6 to 8
- Set B: cards with numbers from 1 to 9

1 Player 1 picks a card from Set A and a card from Set B.

2 Player 1 multiplies the two numbers. The other players check the answer.

8 × 6 = 48

3 If their answer is correct, Player 1 can fill in the box on the worksheet. If it is incorrect, they must leave the box blank.

×	1	2	3	4	5	6	7	8	9
8						48			
7		21							
6				30					

4 Return the cards to their sets and shuffle them. Take turns to play.

The first player to fill all the boxes on their worksheet wins!

Practice Book 3B, p.9

68

Learning objectives: Multiplying by 9

Pupils will be able to:

- recall multiplication concepts in groups of 9 and multiplying by 9
- use the 'finger counting' method to find the nine times table facts
- write multiplication sentences involving 9, given different problem situations
- commit the nine times table facts to memory

Key concepts

- The 'group and item' concept is used for the multiplication facts of 9.
- Repeated addition is used for multiplication.

Thinking skills

- Associating
- Relating
- Identifying relationships

Additional activity

- Ask pupils to look at the ones digits of the multiples of 9.

  9, 18, 27, 3**6**, 45

  54, 63, 72, 81, **9**0

  99, 108 ...

  Help them to see that the digits make a repeating pattern: 9, 8, 7, 6, 5, 4, 3, 2, 1, 0, 9, 8 ...

- Encourage them to observe that digits of the multiples of 9 add up to 9 or a multiple of 9. E.g.,

  10 × 9 = 90 and 9 + 0 = **9**

  12 × 9 = 108 and 1 + 0 + 8 = **9**

Teaching sequence

① and **②**

- Ask pupils to recall the concept of multiplication as groups of items.
- Demonstrate the 'finger-counting' strategy using fingers to help pupils recall the multiplication facts.
- Use this strategy to show how to find all the multiplication facts of 9 up to 10 × 9.
- Ask pupils to practise the strategy in small groups.

Let's Learn!

Multiplying by 9

①

The finger counting method is another way of multiplying. This method is only used for the 9 times table.

a 1 × 9 = 9

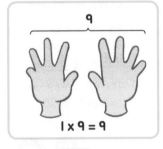

9

1 × 9 = 9

b 2 × 9 = 18

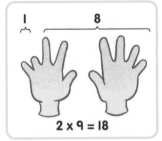

1   8

2 × 9 = 18

c 3 × 9 = 27

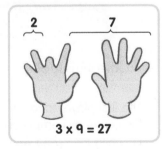

2   7

3 × 9 = 27

Bend your third finger.
3 × 9 = 27

② Use the finger counting method to find the answers.

a 5 × 9 = 45   **b** 6 × 9 = 54

69

Thinking skills

- Recalling
- Applying multiplication facts

What you will need

- Multiplication question cards of 6, 7, 8 and 9 times tables (see Photocopy master 9 on page 271)
- Number board (see Photocopy master 9 on page 270)

Teaching sequence

3 *Game*

- The objective of this activity is to help pupils to practise multiplication facts of 6, 7, 8 and 9.
- Prepare packs of multiplication question cards for the 6, 7, 8 and 9 times tables.
- Make copies of the number board.
- Ask pupils to play the game in groups of 4.
  Give each group a pack of multiplication question cards for the 6, 7, 8 and 9 times tables and a number board. Give each player eight counters. Each player's counters should be a different colour.
- Ask pupils to follow the instructions in the textbook to play the game.
- The first player to reach the centre is the winner.

Unit 5 Multiplying by 6, 7, 8 and 9

Game

3 **Get to the centre!**

How to play:

| Each player chooses a path and puts a counter in the corner box.

2 Player I picks a question card and works out the answer. The other players check the answer.

For example:

$6 \times 5 = \boxed{}$.

The answer in this example is 30.

3 Player I checks to see if the answer is on their path. If it is, they put a counter on the answer on the number board.
If not, they can't put a counter on the number board.

4 Take turns to play.

The first player to reach the centre by completely covering their path with counters wins!

Players: 4
You will need:
- question cards for 6, 7, 8 and 9 times tables
- number board
- 8 counters each

Independent work

Practice 4 in Practice Book 3B,
pp 11 to 12.

4 Answer these questions.

a 9, 18, 27, (36), (45), (54)

b 36, 45, 54, (63), (72), (81)

c 2 × 9 18

d 9 × 3 27

e 4 × 9 36

f 9 × 5 45

g 6 × 9 54

h 9 × 7 63

5 9 times table

1 × 9 = 9	2 × 9 = 18	3 × 9 = 27	4 × 9 = 36	5 × 9 = 45
6 × 9 = 54	7 × 9 = 63	8 × 9 = 72	9 × 9 = 81	10 × 9 = 90

Can you remember the
6, 7, 8 and 9 times tables?

Practice Book 3B, p.11

Make the 9 times table cards as shown below and play a game of "Snap" with your child.

9	18	27	36	45	54	63	72	81	90
1 × 9	2 × 9	3 × 9	4 × 9	5 × 9	6 × 9	7 × 9	8 × 9	9 × 9	10 × 9

Whenever the number and the number sentence match, call "snap" and keep the cards.
The winner is the player with the most cards. You can also make cards of the 6, 7 and 8
times tables.

71

Teaching sequence

4 and **5**

• Ask pupils to work in pairs to work through the questions using the 'finger-counting' strategy.

• Pupils should check each other's answers.

Learning objectives:
Short cut method for multiplying by 6, 7, 8 and 9

Pupils will be able to:

- use the 'connecting fact' strategy starting from 5 × 6 to find more difficult facts of 6
- use the 'connecting fact' strategy starting from 5 × 7 to find more difficult facts of 7
- use the 'connecting fact' strategy starting from 5 × 8 to find more difficult facts of 8

- use the 'connecting fact' strategy starting from 5 × 9 to find more difficult facts of 9

Key concept

The relating facts concept is used to find a more difficult multiplication fact.

Thinking skills

- Associating
- Relating
- Identifying relationships

Additional activity

Show another short cut to find 7 × 8.

Recall a sequence of numbers: 5, 6, 7, 8

56 = 7 × 8   or   7 × 8 = 56

Encourage pupils to see the pattern of numbers for these multiplication facts.

Teaching sequence

- Show pupils the strategy in the textbook to find 6 × 6 from 5 × 6.

- Ask pupils to work on 6 × 7 starting from 5 × 7. Emphasise that 6 × 7 is the same as 5 × 7 and 1 more group of 7.
  Start with 5 × 7 = 35
  6 × 7 is 6 groups of 7
  (It is 1 group of 6 more than 5 × 7 = 35)
  6 × 7 = (5 groups of 7) +
       (1 more group of 7)
       = 35 + 7 = 42

- Ask pupils to work on 7 × 8 starting from 5 × 8. Emphasise that 7 × 8 is the same as 5 × 8 and 2 more groups of 8.
  7 × 8 is 7 groups of 8
  = 2 groups of 8 more than
    5 groups of 8
  = 40 + 8 + 8 = 56

- Ask pupils to find 7 × 9. They should start from 5 × 9.
  7 × 9 is 7 groups of 9
  = 5 groups of 9
    + 2 groups of 9
  = 45 + 18
  = 63

Unit 5 Multiplying by 6, 7, 8 and 9

Let's Learn!

Short cut method for multiplying by 6, 7, 8 and 9

① 6 × 6 = ?

Start with 5 groups of 6.
5 × 6 = 30

6 × 6 is 6 groups of 6.
It is 1 group of 6 more than 5 × 6.
6 × 6 = 30 + 6
      = 36

> 6 × 6 is the same as adding 1 group of 6 to 30.

② 6 × 7 is 6 groups of 7.

6 × 7 = 35 + [7]

= [42]

> Start with 5 groups of 7.
> 5 × 7 = 35

③ 7 × 8 = ?
Start with 5 groups of 8.
5 × 8 = 40

7 × 8 is 7 groups of 8.
It is 2 groups of 8 more than 5 × 8.

7 × 8 = 40 + [8] + [8]

= [56]

④ 7 × 9 is 7 groups of 9.

7 × 9 = 45 + [9] + [9]

= [63]

> Start with 5 groups of 9.
> 5 × 9 = 45

72

Objective of activity

Pupils will be able to discover the pattern of multiples of 5:

(a) whenever an even number is multiplied by 5, it has 0 as its ones digit

(b) whenever an odd number is multiplied by 5, it has 5 as its ones digit

---

Multiplying by 6, 7, 8 and 9 **Unit 5**

5 $8 \times 9 = 45 + \boxed{9} + \boxed{9} + \boxed{9}$

$\qquad = \boxed{72}$

6 $9 \times 9 = 90 - 9$

$\qquad = \boxed{81}$

Start with 10 groups of 9.
$10 \times 9 = 90$

Practice Book 3B, p.13 and 15

Let's Explore!

7 **a** Multiply each number by 5.

	2	4	6	8	10
× 5	10	20	30	40	50

Do you see any pattern in your answers? Yes

What pattern do you see? When we multiply 5 by a number with 2, 4, 6, 8 and 0 in the ones place, we get an answer with 0 in the ones place.

b Now multiply each number by 5.

	1	3	5	7	9
× 5	5	15	25	35	45

Do you see any pattern in your answers? Yes

What pattern do you see? When we multiply 5 by a number with 1, 3, 5, 7 and 9 in the ones place, we get an answer with 5 in the ones place.

73

Teaching sequence

5

• Ask pupils to find 8×9.
  They should start from 5×9.
  $8 \times 9 = 5$ groups of 9 +
  $\qquad\qquad$ 3 groups of 9
  $\qquad = 45 + 9 + 9 + 9 = 72$

6

• Explain to pupils that they can begin from a greater fact, such as 10×9. Then 9×9 is one group of 9 less than 10×9.
  $9 \times 9 = 9$ groups of 9
  $\qquad = 1$ group of 9 less than
  $\qquad\qquad$ 10 groups of 9
  $\qquad = 10 \times 9 - 9$
  $\qquad = 90 - 9 = 81$

7 *Let's Explore!*

• Pupils will be able to see the pattern: when an even number is multiplied by 5, it always ends with 0.

• When an odd number is multiplied by 5, it always ends with 5.

Learning objectives:
Division: finding the number of items in each group

Pupils will be able to:

- recall division concepts in finding the number of items in each group
- find division facts by recalling multiplication facts
- relate division and multiplication facts
- write division facts from given multiplication facts

- write multiplication facts from given division facts
- write division sentences involving 6, 7, 8 or 9, given different problem situations

Key concepts

- Division is the inverse of multiplication.
- Division involves distribution of a set of items equally into some groups by relating multiplication facts.

Thinking skills

- Associating
- Relating
- Identifying relationships

Teaching sequence

- Read out, explain and interpret the question.
- Relate the problem situation to the concept of division.
- Demonstrate with concrete representations the division of 42 cubes into 6 equal groups to find the number of cubes in each group.
- Explain the strategy to find division facts: recall and relate multiplication facts.
- Division facts can be obtained by recalling related multiplication facts of 6. '6, 12, 18, 24, 30, 36, 42...'
- To divide 42 cubes into 6 equal groups, we write:

    42 ÷ 6 = _____

    Then recall related facts:
    6 × ___ = 42 or
    ___ × 6 = 42

    Recalling or using 'skip-counting', pupils should be able to find the answer:
    6 × 7 = 42

Unit 5 Multiplying by 6, 7, 8 and 9

Let's Learn!

Division: finding the number of items in each group

Divide 42 cubes into 6 equal groups.

How many cubes are there in each group?

Think of multiplication:
6 × 7 = 42
So 42 ÷ 6 = 7.

42 ÷ 6 = 7

There are 7 cubes in each group.

74

Additional activity

Ask pupils to work in pairs. Pupil A says a number, e.g., 24. Pupil B then writes three sentences related to 24, such as:

$$3 \times 8 = 24$$
$$8 \times 3 = 24$$
$$24 \div 3 = 8$$

Pupils take turns to say the number and write the sentences.

Multiplying by 6, 7, 8 and 9 **Unit 5**

2 Divide 48 marbles into 8 equal groups.
How many marbles are there in each group?

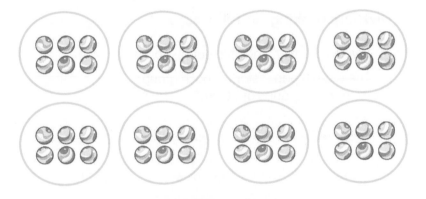

Think of multiplication:
$8 \times 6 = 48$
So $48 \div 8 = \boxed{6}$.

$48 \div 8 = \boxed{6}$

There are $\boxed{6}$ marbles in each group.

3 Divide 35 cubes into 7 equal groups.
How many cubes are there in each group? 5 cubes

4 Divide 72 beads into 8 equal groups.
How many beads are there in each group? 9 beads

Practice Book 3B, p.17

75

Teaching sequence

2

- Ask pupils to follow the same procedure as in **1**:
  recall a related fact and solve using 'finger skip-counting' if they have not mastered the multiplication table.

- Divide 48 marbles into 8 equal groups. Pupils should write a division fact and two related multiplication facts. Pupils are expected to write the following:
  $48 \div 8 = $ _____,
  $8 \times$ _____ $= 48$ and
  _____ $\times 8 = 48$

3 and **4**

- Ask pupils to work in pairs to recall multiplication facts and relate them to division facts.

- Pupils should check each other's answers.

Learning objectives: Division: making equal groups

Pupils will be able to:

- recall division concepts in finding the number of groups
- find division facts by recalling multiplication facts
- relate division and multiplication facts
- write division facts from given multiplication facts
- write multiplication facts from given division facts
- write division sentences involving 6, 7, 8 or 9, given different problem situations

Key concepts

- The 'group and item' concept in multiplication is applied.
- Relating multiplication and division using the 'group and item' concept is applied.

Thinking skills

- Associating
- Relating
- Identifying relationships

Teaching sequence

- Read out, explain and interpret the question.
  Relate the question to the concept of division.
- Demonstrate with concrete representations the division of 56 paper stars into groups of 8 paper stars each.
- Relate the total number of paper stars to the number of groups and the number of items in each group.
  The division sentence is

$$56 \div 8 = \underline{\qquad}$$

| Total number of paper stars | Number of items in each group | Number of groups |

- Recall a multiplication fact relating 56, 8 and another number.
- Demonstrate the strategy to find the division fact using the 'skip-counting' method in multiplication.
- Since 8 × 7 = 56, the unknown number is 7. There are 7 groups of paper stars and each group has 8 paper stars.
- **Note**: Summarise the difference between this question and the previous division questions.

Let's Learn!

Division: making equal groups

1. Divide 56 paper stars into equal groups.

   There are 8 paper stars in each group.
   How many groups are there?

Think of multiplication:
7 × 8 = 56
So 56 ÷ 8 = 7.

$56 \div 8 = 7$

There are 7 groups.

76

Independent work

Practice 8 in Practice Book 3B,
pp 19 to 20.

2 Divide 54 buttons into equal groups.
There are 6 buttons in each group.
How many groups are there?

$54 \div 6 = \boxed{9}$

There are $\boxed{9}$ groups.

Think of multiplication:

$\boxed{9} \times 6 = 54$

So $54 \div 6 = \boxed{9}$.

Activity

3 Think of a division story by arranging 6, 7, 8 or 9 objects
into groups.
Ask your partner to find the answer to your division story.

Example

Hardeep buys 36 pencils.
He puts 9 pencils into each pencil case.
$36 \div 9 = 4$
There are 4 pencil cases.

4 Divide 64 photos into some frames.
Each frame has 8 photos.
How many frames are there?

Practice Book 3B, p.19

77

8 frames

Teaching sequence

2

- Ask pupils to read and interpret the question and then write the division fact and find the answer.

- Pupils are expected to write $54 \div 6 = \underline{}$ (use multiplication fact of $6 \times 9 = 54$)

3

- Revise the two concepts of division: 'group and item' to find the number of
  1) items
  2) groups.

- Explain and relate one of these concepts to the example given in the textbook.

- Ask pupils to tell stories using division facts in 6, 7, 8 or 9 by applying the two concepts explained earlier.

- Collect and display their stories.

4

- Ask pupils to work on this question to ensure they have understood the division concept.

Unit 5: Multiplying by 6, 7, 8 and 9   **133**

Objective of activity
Pupils will be able to apply multiplication and division facts to find the numbers.

Independent work
Challenging Practice and *Problem Solving* in Practice Book 3B, pp 21 to 22.

Thinking skills
- Associating
- Relating
- Identifying relationships

Teaching sequence

5 *Put On Your Thinking Caps!*

- Demonstrate the 'working back' concept using simple examples in addition and subtraction.
- Introduce this strategy in multiplication and division.
- Another strategy is to make a list of multiplication facts and pick the one that satisfies the given condition.
- Relate multiplication and division facts of 9.
- Recall the 9 times table. (9, 18, 27, 36, 45, 54, 63, 72...)
  ___ × 9 = 72 or
  72 ÷ 9 = 8
- Ask pupils to work on the problem using one of the strategies above.
- Since the answers are between 45 and 60, ensure pupils list multiples of 8. The answers have to be 48 and 56.
  ___ × 8 = 48
  48 ÷ 8 = 6
  ___ × 8 = 56
  56 ÷ 8 = 7

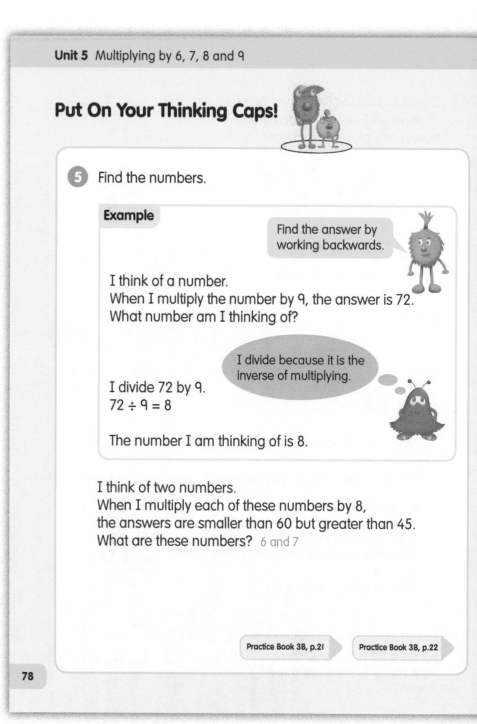

Unit 5 Multiplying by 6, 7, 8 and 9

Put On Your Thinking Caps!

5 Find the numbers.

> **Example**
>
> Find the answer by working backwards.
>
> I think of a number.
> When I multiply the number by 9, the answer is 72.
> What number am I thinking of?
>
> I divide because it is the inverse of multiplying.
>
> I divide 72 by 9.
> 72 ÷ 9 = 8
>
> The number I am thinking of is 8.

I think of two numbers.
When I multiply each of these numbers by 8, the answers are smaller than 60 but greater than 45.
What are these numbers? 6 and 7

Practice Book 3B, p.21   Practice Book 3B, p.22

78

Unit 5

Multiplying by 6, 7, 8 and 9

Date: _____

1 Count in sixes. Fill in the spaces.

a 6, 12, 18, _24_ , 30 , 36 , 42 , 48 , 54 , 60

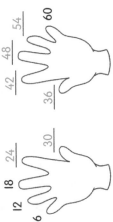

b 18, _24_ , 30 , 36 , 42 , 48 , 54 , 60

2 Fill in the spaces.

a 8 sixes = 8 × _6_

b 5 × 6 = _5_ _____ sixes

c 7 + 7 + 7 + 7 + 7 + 7 = 6 × _7_

d 6 + 6 + 6 + 6 + 6 + 6 + 6 = 7 × _6_

e 10 × 6 = 6 × _10_

f 4 sixes = 6 + 6 + 6 + _6_

INSPIRE MATHS

PRACTICE BOOK 3B

Koogol

Googol

Zoogol

Toogol

Noogol

Ooogol

Consultant and author
Dr Fong Ho Kheong

Authors
Chelvi Ramakrishnan and Michelle Choo

UK consultants
Carole Skinner, Simon d'Angelo and Elizabeth Gibbs

Date: _____

Practice 2 Multiplying by 7: skip-counting

1 Count in sevens.
Fill in the spaces.

a 7, 14, 21, __28__, __35__, __42__

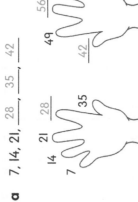

28, __35__, 42, 49, __56__, 63, __70__

b 21, __28__, 35, __42__, 49, __56__, 63, 70

2 Fill in the spaces.

a 6 sevens = 6 × __7__

b 9 × 7 = __9__ sevens

c 5 + 5 + 5 + 5 + 5 + 5 + 5 = 7 × __5__

d 7 + 7 + 7 + 7 + 7 + 7 + 7 = 5 × __7__

e 10 × 7 = 7 × __10__

f 4 sevens = 7 + 7 + 7 + __7__

---

3 Millie has mixed up all of her socks.
Help her sort them out by matching the correct pairs.

36   12   30   24   54   42   48

60   18   2 × 6   3 × 6   4 × 6   5 × 6   6 × 6   7 × 6   8 × 6   9 × 6   10 × 6

Practice 3 Multiplying by 8: skip-counting

$1 \times 8 = 8$
$2 \times 8 = 16$
$3 \times 8 = 24$

1 Count in eights.
Fill in the spaces.

a 8, 16, 24, 32 , 40 , 48 , 56

b 40, 48, 56 , 64 , 72 , 80

c 8, 16 , 24 , 32 , 40 , 48 , 56 , 64

d 8 , 16 , 24, 32, 40, 48 , 56 , 64 , 72

2 Fill in the spaces.

a 8 eights = 8 × 8

b 3 eights = 3 × 8

c 6 + 6 + 6 + 6 + 6 + 6 + 6 + 6 = 8 × 6

d 8 + 8 + 8 + 8 + 8 + 8 = 6 × 8

e 5 × 8 = 8 × 5

f 4 eights = 8 + 8 + 8 + 8

3 Match the teabags to the correct cups.

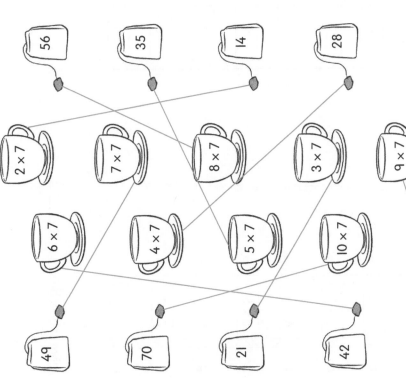

Practice 4 Multiplying by 9

1 Find the answers.

a $2 \times 9 =$ __18__ 　　　b $4 \times 9 =$ __36__

c $5 \times 9 =$ __45__ 　　　d $3 \times 9 =$ __27__

e $7 \times 9 =$ __63__ 　　　f $6 \times 9 =$ __54__

g $8 \times 9 =$ __72__ 　　　h $9 \times 9 =$ __81__

i $10 \times 9 =$ __90__ 　　　j $1 \times 9 =$ __9__

2 Fill in the spaces.

a 3 nines = $3 \times$ __9__

b 4 nines = __4__ $\times 9$

c $9 + 9 + 9 + 9 + 9 + 9 = 6 \times$ __9__

d $6 + 6 + 6 + 6 + 6 + 6 = 9 \times$ __6__

e $9 \times 8 = 8 \times$ __9__

f 8 nines = $9 + 9 + 9 + 9 + 9 +$ __9__ $+$ __9__ $+$ __9__

3 Match.

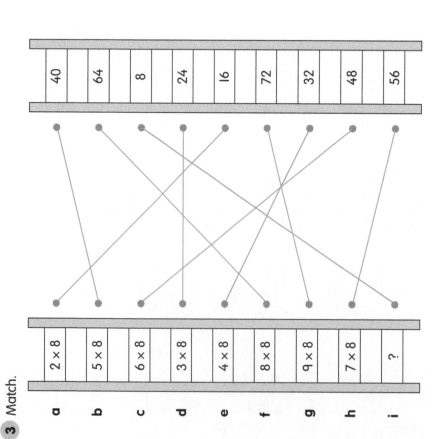

a 2×8

b 5×8

c 6×8

d 3×8

e 4×8

f 8×8

g 9×8

h 7×8

i ?

40　64　8　24　16　72　32　48　56

What should be in box i? __1×8__

Practice 5 — Short cut method for multiplying by 6, 7, 8 and 9

1 Fill in the spaces.

a 6 × 4 = ___6___ groups of 4
= 5 groups of 4 + ___1___ group of 4
= ___20___ + ___4___
= ___24___

b 7 × 4 = ___7___ groups of 4
= 5 groups of 4 + ___2___ groups of 4
= ___20___ + ___8___
= ___28___

c 8 × 4 = ___8___ groups of 4
= 5 groups of 4 + ___3___ groups of 4
= ___20___ + ___12___
= ___32___

---

3 Match the balls to the correct baskets.

Baskets: 9 + 9 + 9 + 9 + 9 + 9 + 9 + 9 + 9 ; 7 × 9 ; 27 ; 9 + 9 + 9 + 9 + 9 + 9 + 9 ; 9 + 9 + 9 + 9 + 9 + 9 ; 4 nines ; 9 + 9

Balls: 3 nines ; 9 × 9 ; 9 × 5 ; 63 ; 36 ; 2 × 9 ; 54

Practice 6

Multiplying by 6, 7, 8 and 9: word problems

1 Jack has 8 toy lorries.
Each toy lorry has 6 wheels.
How many wheels are there altogether?

$8 \times 6 = 48$

There are ___48___ wheels altogether.

2 The baker buys 7 bags of flour.
Each bag of flour costs £2.
How much does the baker spend altogether?

$7 \times £2 = £$ ___14___   14

The baker spends £ ___14___ altogether.

3 An octagon has 8 sides.
How many sides do 5 octagons
have altogether?

$5 \times 8 = 40$

5 octagons have ___40___ sides altogether.

---

2 Fill in the spaces.

a $5 \times 6 =$ ___30___ → ___30___ $+ 6 + 6$

$7 \times 6 =$ ___ $=$ ___42___

b $5 \times 7 =$ ___35___ → ___35___ $+ 7 + 7$

$7 \times 7 =$ ___ $=$ ___49___

c $10 \times 7 =$ ___70___ → ___70___ $- 7$

$9 \times 7 =$ ___ $=$ ___63___

d $10 \times 9 =$ ___90___ → ___90___ $- 9$

$9 \times 9 =$ ___ $=$ ___81___

3 Use the short cut method to multiply.

a $8 \times 6 =$ ___48___

b $7 \times 8 =$ ___56___

c $6 \times 9 =$ ___54___

d $9 \times 8 =$ ___72___

Practice 7 Division: finding the number of items in each group

1 Look at the multiplication sentence.
Write two division sentences.

Example   6 × 7 = 42

$$42 \div \underline{6} = \underline{7}$$

$$42 \div \underline{7} = \underline{6}$$

a   9 × 5 = 45

$$45 \div \underline{9} = \underline{5}$$

$$45 \div \underline{5} = \underline{9}$$

b   7 × 9 = 63

$$63 \div \underline{7} = \underline{9}$$

$$63 \div \underline{9} = \underline{7}$$

c   8 × 6 = 48

$$48 \div \underline{8} = \underline{6}$$

$$48 \div \underline{6} = \underline{8}$$

---

4 Ella has 4 pages of stickers.
There are 9 stickers on each page.
How many stickers are there altogether?

$$\underline{4} \times 9 = \underline{36}$$

There are ___36___ stickers altogether.

5 Look at the pictures.

I bowl of salad
£3

I slice of pizza
£4

I pie
£2

Write a multiplication story in the space below.
Use the 6, 7, 8 or 9 times table.

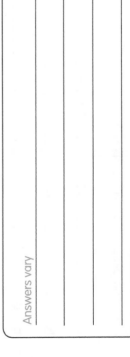

Answers vary

Practice 8   Division: making equal groups

1 Use times tables to find the answers.

a   ___5___ × 9 = 45   b   ___9___ × 7 = 63

45 ÷ 9 = __5__   63 ÷ 7 = __9__

c   6 × ___9___ = 54   d   8 × ___7___ = 56

54 ÷ 6 = __9__   56 ÷ 8 = __7__

2 Divide.

a   21 ÷ 7 = __3__   b   36 ÷ 9 = __4__

c   72 ÷ 8 = __9__   d   42 ÷ 7 = __6__

e   48 ÷ 6 = __8__   f   64 ÷ 8 = __8__

---

2 Use multiplication. Then complete the division sentence.

a   6 × __7__ = 42   So 42 ÷ 6 = __7__

b   7 × __7__ = 49   So 49 ÷ 7 = __7__

c   8 × __6__ = 48   So 48 ÷ 8 = __6__

d   9 × __5__ = 45   So 45 ÷ 9 = __5__

3 Mr Davies fits 9 lorries with 54 wheels. Each lorry has the same number of wheels. How many wheels does each lorry have?

54 ÷ 9 = 6

Each lorry has __6__ wheels.

4 Farha collects 63 shells on the beach. She puts them equally into 7 boxes. How many shells are there in each box?

63 ÷ 7 = 9

There are __9__ shells in each box.

Date: _____

Challenging Practice

1. Fill in the spaces.

   a   6, 12, 18, 24, __30__, ___, 36, 42, 48, 54, 60
   b   7, 14, 21, __28__, 35, 42, 49, 56, 63
   c   8, 16, 24, __32__, 40, 48, 56, 64, 72
   d   9, 18, 27, __36__, 45, 54, 63, 72, 81

2. Colour the odd one out in each box. Give a reason for your answer. Use the numbers in Question 1 to help you.

   63, 81, 45, 54, 28, 72
   Reason: It is the odd one out because it is not found in the __9__ times table.

   72, 64, 40, 56, 36, 24
   Reason: It is the odd one out because it is not found in the __8__ times table.

   49, 21, 63, 32, 42, 35
   Reason: It is the odd one out because it is not found in the __7__ times table.

   54, 48, 42, 24, 30, 35
   Reason: It is the odd one out because it is not found in the __6__ times table.

---

3. A baker makes 30 cakes.
   He puts 6 cakes into each box.
   How many boxes does he use?

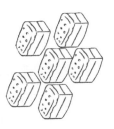

   $30 \div 6 = 5$

   He uses __5__ boxes.

4. A fish tank can hold 8 litres of water.
   How many tanks are needed to hold 64 litres of water?

   $64 \div 8 = 8$

   __8__ tanks are needed to hold 64 litres of water.

5. Omar puts 36 marbles away into bags.
   Each bag has 9 marbles.
   How many bags are there?

   $36 \div 9 = 4$

   There are __4__ bags.

Problem Solving

1. I am a 2-digit number.
I am less than 50.
Count in sixes and you will find me!
Divide my tens digit by 2 and you will find my ones digit.
What number am I?

I am ___42___ .

Number	Tens digit	Ones digit	Check
12	1	2	✗
18	1	8	✗
24	2	4	✗
30	3	0	✗
36	3	6	✗
42	4	2	✓
48	4	8	✗

Unit 6: Multiplication

Week	Learning Objectives	Thinking Skills	Resources
3	**(1) Multiplication without regrouping** Pupils will be able to: • use concrete representations in a place value chart to show multiplication of a 2-digit or 3-digit number by 2, 3, 4 or 5 without regrouping • multiply a 2-digit or 3-digit number by 2, 3, 4 or 5 without regrouping in horizontal or vertical format • know that the 'product' is the result of multiplying two numbers • carry out the multiplication procedure by multiplying numbers from right to left	• Classifying • Identifying relationships • Relating	• Pupil Textbook 3A, pp 79 to 82 • Practice Book 3B, pp 23 to 26 • Teacher's Guide 3A, pp 147 to 150
3	**(2) Multiplication with regrouping in ones, tens and hundreds** Pupils will be able to: • use concrete representations in a place value chart to show multiplication of a 2-digit or 3-digit number by 2, 3, 4 or 5 with regrouping in ones, tens and hundreds • multiply a 2-digit or 3-digit number by a 1-digit number with regrouping in ones, tens and hundreds in horizontal or vertical format • carry out the multiplication procedure by multiplying numbers from right to left with regrouping in ones, tens and hundreds	• Classifying • Identifying relationships • Relating • Sequencing	• Pupil Textbook 3A, pp 83 to 87 • Practice Book 3B, pp 27 to 30 • Teacher's Guide 3A, pp 151 to 155

Unit 6: Multiplication

Week	Learning Objectives	Thinking Skills	Resources
3	**(3) Multiplication with regrouping in ones, tens, hundreds and thousands** Pupils will be able to: • use concrete representations in a place value chart to show multiplication of a 2-digit or 3-digit number by 2, 3, 4 or 5 with regrouping in ones, tens, hundreds and thousands • multiply a 2-digit or 3-digit number by a 1-digit number with regrouping in ones, tens, hundreds and thousands in horizontal or vertical format • carry out the multiplication procedure by multiplying numbers from right to left with regrouping in ones, tens, hundreds and thousands *Let's Explore!* Pupils will be able to apply the 'guess and check' and deduction strategies to find the greatest and the smallest product by multiplying a 1-digit number and a 3-digit number with regrouping.	• Classifying • Identifying relationships • Relating • Sequencing • Deduction Heuristic for problem solving: • Guess and check	• Pupil Textbook 3A, pp 88 to 91 • Practice Book 3B, pp 31 to 36 • Teacher's Guide 3A, pp 156 to 159
4	*Put On Your Thinking Caps!* Pupils will be able to apply the 'using pattern' strategy and the multiplication concept to find the sum of a set of consecutive numbers.	• Applying the pattern strategy and seeing connections between numbers	• Pupil Textbook 3A, p 92 • Practice Book 3B, pp 37 to 38 • Teacher's Guide 3A, p 160
	Review 3		• Practice Book 3B, pp 39 to 42

Multiplication

**Learning objectives:
Multiplication without
regrouping**

Pupils will be able to:

- use concrete representations
  in a place value chart to show
  multiplication of a 2-digit or
  3-digit number by 2, 3, 4 or 5
  without regrouping

- multiply a 2-digit or 3-digit
  number by 2, 3, 4 or 5 without
  regrouping in horizontal or
  vertical format
- know that the 'product' is
  the result of multiplying two
  numbers
- carry out the multiplication
  procedure by multiplying
  numbers from right to left

Key concepts

- A number up to 1000 can be
  conceptualised as the sum
  of its values in the ones, tens
  and hundreds places.
- Multiplication of a 2-digit
  number or a 3-digit number
  by a 1-digit number is the sum
  of multiplying values from
  different places.

Unit
6 Multiplication

Let's Learn!

Multiplication without regrouping

❶ 12 × 3 = ?

Tens	Ones
	▢ ▢
	▢ ▢
	▢ ▢

Tens	Ones
▭	▢ ▢
▭	▢ ▢
▭	▢ ▢

First multiply the **ones** by 3.

```
  1 2
×   3
─────
    6   2 ones × 3 = 6 ones
```

12 × 3 = 36

Then multiply the **tens** by 3.

```
  1 2
×   3
─────
  3 6   1 ten × 3 = 3 tens
```

When we multiply
12 by 3, we get the
product of 12 and 3.

36 is the product
of 12 and 3.

Teaching sequence

①

- Explain the concept of a
  2-digit number as a sum of
  the values of the ones and
  tens. Illustrate this idea using
  a place value chart.
- Demonstrate 12 × 3 by
  multiplying the 2 ones by
  3 then the 1 ten by 3 using
  counters on place value chart.
- Emphasise that multiplying
  the ones (in this case 2) by 3
  is the same as (2 + 2 + 2): a
  repeated addition of 2s.
  First multiply the ones.

```
  1 2
×   3
─────
    6
```

2 **ones** × 3 = (2 + 2 + 2)
           = 6 ones
Then multiply the tens.

```
  1 2
×   3
─────
  3 6
```

1 **ten** × 3 = (10 + 10 + 10)
           = 3 tens
           = 30

- Emphasise that multiplying
  1 ten by 3 is the same as
  (10 + 10 + 10): a repeated
  addition of 10s.
- Explain the word 'product'.
  The product of 12 and 3 is
  12 × 3 = 36.

79

Thinking skills
- Classifying
- Identifying relationships
- Relating

What you will need
- Place value charts
- Base ten equipment or counters

Teaching sequence

- Using the same procedures as in ①, explain multiplication of a 3-digit number by a 1-digit number without regrouping.
- Use concrete representations and a place value chart to represent 341.
- Demonstrate the steps to multiply each place value from right to left by 2 and represent the results in the place value chart. The procedures are shown in the textbook.
- First multiply the ones by 2, then the tens and finally the hundreds.

Multiply the ones by 2.

$$\begin{array}{r} 3\ 4\ 1 \\ \times\qquad 2 \\ \hline 2 \end{array}$$

1 **one** × 2 = 1 + 1
$\qquad$ = **2 ones**

Multiply the tens by 2.

$$\begin{array}{r} 3\ 4\ 1 \\ \times\qquad 2 \\ \hline 8\ 2 \end{array}$$

4 **tens** × 2 = 40 + 40
$\qquad$ = **8 tens**

Multiply the hundreds by 2.

$$\begin{array}{r} 3\ 4\ 1 \\ \times\qquad 2 \\ \hline 6\ 8\ 2 \end{array}$$

3 **hundreds** × 2 = 300 + 300
$\qquad$ = **6 hundreds**

- **Note**: The prerequisite for this exercise is that pupils have mastered the 2 times table.

Unit 6 Multiplication

 341 × 2 = ?

Hundreds	Tens	Ones

First multiply the **ones** by 2.

$$\begin{array}{r} 3\ 4\ 1 \\ \times\qquad 2 \\ \hline 2 \end{array}$$

1 one × 2 = 2 ones

Hundreds	Tens	Ones

Then multiply the **tens** by 2.

$$\begin{array}{r} 3\ 4\ 1 \\ \times\qquad 2 \\ \hline 8\ 2 \end{array}$$

4 tens × 2 = 8 tens

Hundreds	Tens	Ones

Finally multiply the **hundreds** by 2.

$$\begin{array}{r} 3\ 4\ 1 \\ \times\qquad 2 \\ \hline 6\ 8\ 2 \end{array}$$

3 hundreds × 2 = 6 hundreds

341 × 2 = 682

Additional activity

Ask pupils to work in pairs. Ask them to identify and explain the mistakes in the following:

(1)
```
    2 3
  ×   2
  ─────
    6 4
```

(2)
```
    2 1 3
  ×     3
  ───────
    3 6 9
```

(3)
```
    1 2 4
  ×     2
  ───────
    3 5 8
```

③ 34 × 2 = ?

First multiply the ones by 2.

4 ones × 2 = ⬡8 ones

```
    3   4
  ×     2
  ───────
        8
```

Then multiply the tens by 2.

3 tens × 2 = ⬡6 tens

34 × 2 = ⬡68

```
    3   4
  ×     2
  ───────
    6   8
```

④ 132 × 3 = ?

First multiply the ones by 3.

⬡2 ones × 3 = ⬡6 ones

```
  1   3   2
  ×       3
  ─────────
          6
```

Then multiply the tens by 3.

⬡3 tens × 3 = ⬡9 tens

```
  1   3   2
  ×       3
  ─────────
      9   6
```

Finally multiply the hundreds by 3.

⬡1 hundred × 3 = ⬡3 hundreds

132 × 3 = ⬡396

```
  1   3   2
  ×       3
  ─────────
  3   9   6
```

⑤ Multiply these numbers.

a
```
    2 4
  ×   2
  ─────
   48
```

b
```
    4 0
  ×   2
  ─────
   80
```

c
```
    2 3 2
  ×     3
  ───────
    696
```

d
```
    1 1 2
  ×     4
  ───────
    448
```

81

Teaching sequence

③

• Ask pupils to work in pairs. Ask them to discuss the procedure for vertical multiplication. Ensure they understand the place value concept by going through the steps to find the products in ones and tens. For this question, pupils need to have mastered the 2 times table.

④

• Ask pupils to work in pairs to repeat the procedure in ③.

• For this question, they need to have mastered the 3 times table.

⑤

• For this exercise, pupils can work individually. Ensure that pupils have already mastered the 2, 3 and 4 times tables.

Recalling multiplication facts

What you will need
Worksheets A, B, C & D
(see Photocopy master 10 on
page 272)

Independent work
Practice 1 in Practice Book 3B,
pp 23 to 26.

Teaching sequence

6 *Game*

- The objective of this activity
  is for pupils to come up
  with their own questions by
  choosing cards at random as
  shown in the textbook.
- Prepare worksheets A, B, C
  and D as follows:
  use the worksheet template
  from Photocopy master 4.
  Write down a 3-digit number
  for each of the worksheets
  (e.g., 120, 222, 202, 102, 201,
  210, 111, 220 or 101).
  Make copies of the
  worksheets A, B, C and D.
- Ask pupils to play in groups
  of 2 to 4. Give each player
  1 worksheet: A, B, C or D.
  Ask pupils to write 1 set of
  numbers 2, 3 and 4 on small
  pieces of paper/card.
- Each player selects a card to
  get a number. Each player can
  use each number only once.
- The player places the number
  on the box in the worksheet
  and finds the product.
- Players play three rounds
  each. The player with the most
  correct answers wins.

Unit 6 Multiplication

Game

6 **Find the product!**

How to play:

Each player is given
one worksheet
A, B, C or D.

WORKSHEET A			
	H	T	O
	2	2	1
×			

1 Make number cards by writing
2, 3 and 4 on pieces of paper.
Cut them into square pieces.
Place them face down on the
table and shuffle.

2 Pick a card to get a
number. Each number
can be used only once
by each player.

3 Put the number card on your
worksheet. Find the product of
the number on the worksheet
and the number from the card.
The other players check
the answer.

WORKSHEET A			
	H	T	O
	2	2	1
×			3

4 Put the number card
back with the other
cards for the next
player to select.

> The player with the most
> correct answers wins!

5 Take turns to play.
Play three rounds.

Practice Book 3B, p.23

Players: 2 to 4
You will need:
- worksheets A, B, C and D
- number cards with
  numbers 2, 3 and 4

Home Maths Play this game at home with your child. Give them worksheets with 3-digit numbers that do not
need regrouping when multiplied by 2, 3, or 4. For example, 122, 210, 112 and 102.

82

Learning objectives: Multiplication with regrouping in ones, tens and hundreds

Pupils will be able to:

- use concrete representations in a place value chart to show multiplication of a 2-digit or 3-digit number by 2, 3, 4 or 5 with regrouping in ones, tens and hundreds
- multiply a 2-digit or 3-digit number by a 1-digit number with regrouping in ones, tens and hundreds in horizontal or vertical format
- carry out the multiplication procedure by multiplying numbers from right to left with regrouping in ones, tens and hundreds

Key concepts

- A number up to 1000 can be conceptualised as the sum of its values in the ones, tens and hundreds places.
- Multiplication of a 2-digit number or a 3-digit number by a 1-digit number is the sum of multiplying values from different places.

- Regrouping in ones, tens and hundreds is used in multiplication.

Thinking skills

- Classifying
- Identifying relationships
- Relating
- Sequencing

Let's Learn!

Multiplication with regrouping in ones, tens and hundreds

1 68 × 2 = ?

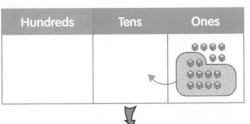

First multiply the **ones** by 2.

```
    6 8
  ×   2
  ─────
      6
      ¹
```

8 ones × 2 = 16 ones

Regroup the ones:
16 ones = 1 ten 6 ones

Then multiply the **tens** by 2.

```
    6 8
  ×   2
  ─────
  1 3 6
  ¹
```
6 tens × 2 = 12 tens

Add the tens:
12 tens + 1 ten = 13 tens

Regroup the tens:
13 tens = 1 hundred 3 tens

68 × 2 = 136

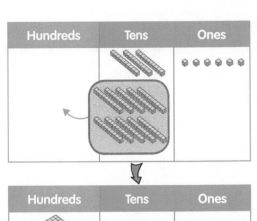

83

Teaching sequence

1

- Demonstrate, using concrete representations and a place value chart, the procedures to find the product of 68 and 2.
- Explain the overall strategy: multiply from right to left; regroup whenever it is necessary.
  Show the procedures with concrete representations, especially the regrouping process.
- Carry out the procedures:

  Step 1:
  Multiply 8 ones by 2 = 16 ones. Show regrouping using base ten equipment. Regroup the ones.
  16 ones = 1 ten 6 ones

  Step 2:
  Multiply 6 tens by 2 = 12 tens. Show regrouping using base ten equipment. Regroup the tens. 12 tens + 1 ten = 13 tens
  13 tens = 1 hundred 3 tens

- 68 × 2 = 1 hundred 3 tens and 6 ones
  = 136

Additional activity

Ask pupils to work in pairs. Ask them to identify and explain the mistakes in the following:

(I)
```
    4 8
  ×   3
  -----
  1 2 4
```

(2)
```
    3 5
  ×   4
  -----
  2 0 0
```

- Ask pupils to work in pairs. Ask them to discuss the procedures for vertical multiplication. Pupils also need to understand the place value concept by going through the steps to find the products in ones and tens. Pupils need to have mastered the 2 times table.

Unit 6 Multiplication

2 69 × 2 = ?

First multiply the ones by 2.

9 ones × 2 = [18] ones

Regroup the ones:

[18] ones = [1] ten [8] ones

Then multiply the tens by 2.

6 tens × 2 = [12] tens

Add the tens:

[12] tens + [1] ten = [13] tens

Regroup the tens:

[13] tens = [1] hundred [3] tens

69 × 2 = [138]

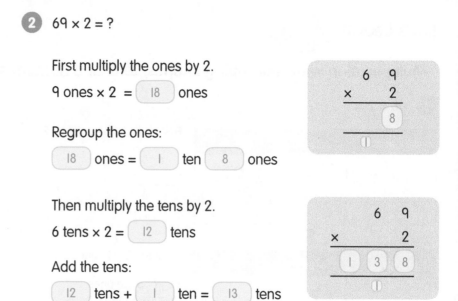

84

3 $146 \times 5 = ?$

Hundreds	Tens	Ones
		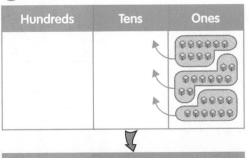

First multiply the **ones** by 5.

```
    1  4  6
 ×        5
 ─────────
          0
       3
```
6 ones × 5 = 30 ones

Hundreds	Tens	Ones
	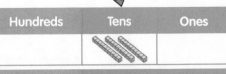	

Regroup the ones:
30 ones = 3 tens

Hundreds	Tens	Ones
	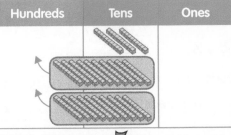	

Then multiply the **tens** by 5.

```
    1  4  6
 ×        5
 ─────────
       3  0
     2 3
```
4 tens × 5 = 20 tens

Add the tens:
20 tens + 3 tens = 23 tens

Hundreds	Tens	Ones
	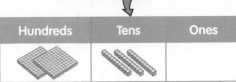	

Regroup the tens:
23 tens = 2 hundreds 3 tens

Hundreds	Tens	Ones
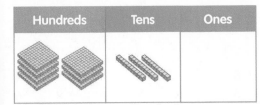		

Finally multiply the **hundreds** by 5.

```
    1  4  6
 ×        5
 ─────────
    7  3  0
     2 3
```
1 hundred × 5 = 5 hundreds

Add the hundreds:
5 hundreds + 2 hundreds
= 7 hundreds

$146 \times 5 = 730$

85

Teaching sequence

- Explain the difference between this question and question **2**.
- Highlight that in both questions, regrouping is required in the ones and tens places.
  In this question, we multiply a 3-digit number by a 1-digit number.
  Follow the same procedure to explain the multiplication processes.

Step 1:
Multiply 6 ones by 5 = 30 ones.
Demonstrate regrouping using base ten equipment.
Regroup the ones.
30 ones = 3 tens 0 ones

Step 2:
Multiply 4 tens by 5 = 20 tens.
Demonstrate regrouping using base ten equipment.
Regroup the tens.
20 tens + 3 tens = 23 tens
23 tens = 2 hundreds 3 tens

Step 3:
Multiply 1 hundred by 5 = 5 hundreds. Then add the hundreds.
5 hundreds + 2 hundreds = 7 hundreds

- $146 \times 5 = 7$ hundreds 3 tens and 0 ones = 730

Unit 6: Multiplication　　153

Ask pupils to work in pairs.
Give each pair some base ten
equipment or counters. Ask
them to show the following,
using concrete representations:

(1) 24 ones = 2 tens 4 ones
                  = I ten I4 ones

(2) 58 ones = 5 tens 8 ones
                  = 4 tens I8 ones

Teaching sequence

- Repeat the procedure as in ③. Pupils need to have mastered the 4 times table.
- Pupils also need to understand the regrouping process before working on the question in the vertical format.

- Pupils should work individually on this problem. Ensure that they have already mastered the 2, 3, 4 and 5 times tables.

Unit 6 Multiplication

 157 × 4 = ?

First multiply the ones by 4.

⎡ 7 ⎤ ones × 4 = ⎡ 28 ⎤ ones

	I	5	7
×			4
			8
		(2)	

Regroup the ones:

⎡ 28 ⎤ ones = ⎡ 2 ⎤ tens ⎡ 8 ⎤ ones

Then multiply the tens by 4.

⎡ 5 ⎤ tens × 4 = ⎡ 20 ⎤ tens

	I	5	7
×			4
		2	8
	(2)	(2)	

Add the tens:

⎡ 20 ⎤ tens + ⎡ 2 ⎤ tens = ⎡ 22 ⎤ tens

Regroup the tens:

⎡ 22 ⎤ tens = ⎡ 2 ⎤ hundreds ⎡ 2 ⎤ tens

Finally multiply the hundreds by 4.

⎡ I ⎤ hundred × 4 = ⎡ 4 ⎤ hundreds

	I	5	7
×			4
6	2	8	
(2)	(2)		

Add the hundreds:

⎡ 4 ⎤ hundreds + ⎡ 2 ⎤ hundreds

= ⎡ 6 ⎤ hundreds

157 × 4 = ⎡ 628 ⎤

⑤ Multiply.

a	3 9 5	**b**	2 7 8	**c**	I 6 8	**d**	2 4 9
×	2	×	3	×	5	×	4
	790		834		840		996

86

Thinking skill

Recalling multiplication facts involving regrouping in ones and tens.

What you will need

Spinner and Question Sheet (see Photocopy master 11 on pages 273 to 274)

Independent work

Practices 2 and 3 in Practice Book 3B, pp 27 to 30.

Game

6 **Spin and multiply!**

How to play:

Each player is given a question sheet.

Players: 2 to 4
You will need:
- a spinner with numbers 2, 3, 4 and 5
- a question sheet for each player

1 Spin the spinner to get a number.

2 Write this number in the box on the question sheet. Work out the answer. The other players check the answer.

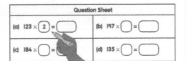

Question Sheet	
(a) 123 × ②= ⬭	(b) 197 × ◯= ⬭
(c) 184 × ◯= ⬭	(d) 135 × ◯= ⬭

3 Take turns to play.
The game ends when every player has completed their question sheet.

The player with the most correct answers wins!

Practice Book 3B, p.27 and 29

87

Teaching sequence

6 *Game*

- In this game, pupils will create their own multiplier using a spinner. This activity provides them with an opportunity to practise multiplication.
- Make a spinner with the numbers 2, 3, 4 and 5 using the Photocopy master, a split pin and a card pointer.
- Ask pupils to play the game in groups. Give each player a question sheet.
- Players should take turns to spin the spinner to get a number.
- Each player writes the number in the box on the question sheet and works out the answer to the multiplication sentence.
- End the game when every player has completed their question sheet. The player with the most correct answers wins.

Learning objectives: Multiplication with regrouping in ones, tens, hundreds and thousands

Pupils will be able to:

- use concrete representations in a place value chart to show multiplication of a 2-digit or 3-digit number by 2, 3, 4 or 5 with regrouping in ones, tens, hundreds and thousands
- multiply a 2-digit or 3-digit number by a 1-digit number with regrouping in ones, tens, hundreds and thousands in horizontal or vertical format

Teaching sequence

- Explain to pupils that this question requires regrouping in thousands as compared to the previous questions.
- Demonstrate, using concrete representations and a place value chart, the procedures to find the product of 656 and 2.
- Carry out the procedures:

Step 1:
Multiply 6 ones by 2 = 12 ones. Demonstrate regrouping using base ten equipment. Regroup the ones.
12 ones = 1 ten 2 ones

Step 2:
Multiply 5 tens by 2 = 10 tens. Demonstrate regrouping using base ten equipment. Regroup the tens.
10 tens + 1 ten = 11 tens
11 tens = 1 hundred 1 ten

- carry out the multiplication procedure by multiplying numbers from right to left with regrouping in ones, tens, hundreds and thousands

Key concepts

- A number up to 1000 can be conceptualised as the sum of its values in the ones, tens and hundreds places.
- Multiplication of a 2-digit number or a 3-digit number by a 1-digit number is the sum of multiplying values from different places.
- Regrouping in ones, tens, hundreds and thousands is used in multiplication.

Unit 6 Multiplication

Let's Learn!

Multiplication with regrouping in ones, tens, hundreds and thousands

 656 × 2 = ?

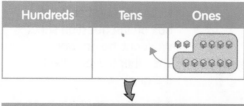

First multiply the **ones** by 2.

$$\begin{array}{r} 6\ 5\ 6 \\ \times\qquad 2 \\ \hline 2 \end{array}$$

6 ones × 2 = 12 ones

Regroup the ones:
12 ones = 1 ten 2 ones

Then multiply the **tens** by 2.

$$\begin{array}{r} 6\ 5\ 6 \\ \times\qquad 2 \\ \hline 1\ 2 \end{array}$$

5 tens × 2 = 10 tens

Add the tens:
10 tens + 1 ten = 11 tens

Regroup the tens:
11 tens = 1 hundred 1 ten

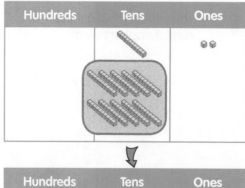

What you will need
- Base ten equipment
- Place value charts

Thinking skills
- Classifying
- Identifying relationships
- Relating
- Sequencing
- Deduction

Heuristic for problem solving
Guess and check

Multiplication **Unit 6**

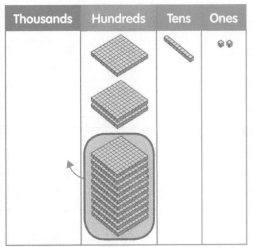

Thousands	Hundreds	Tens	Ones

Finally multiply the **hundreds** by 2.

```
    6  5  6
×          2
─────────────
 1  3  1  2
    ¹  ¹
```

6 hundreds × 2 = 12 hundreds

Add the hundreds:

12 hundreds + 1 hundred
= 13 hundreds

Thousands	Hundreds	Tens	Ones

Regroup the hundreds:
13 hundreds
= 1 thousand 3 hundreds

$656 × 2 = 1312$

We regroup 13 hundreds to get 1 thousand 3 hundreds.

Teaching sequence

Step 3:
Multiply 6 hundreds by 2
= 12 hundreds.
Demonstrate regrouping
using base ten equipment.
Regroup the hundreds.
12 hundreds + 1 hundred
= 13 hundreds
= 1 thousand 3 hundreds

- 656 × 2
  = 1 thousand 3 hundreds
    1 ten and 2 ones
  = 1312

Additional activity

Ask pupils to work in pairs. Give each pair some base ten equipment or counters. Ask them to show the following using concrete representations:

635 ones = 6 hundreds
3 tens 5 ones

= 5 hundreds
13 tens 5 ones

= 5 hundreds
12 tens 15 ones

Teaching sequence

- Ask pupils to work in pairs. Ask them to discuss the procedures for vertical multiplication. Pupils also need to understand the place value concept by going through the steps to find the products in ones and tens. Pupils need to have mastered the 4 times table.

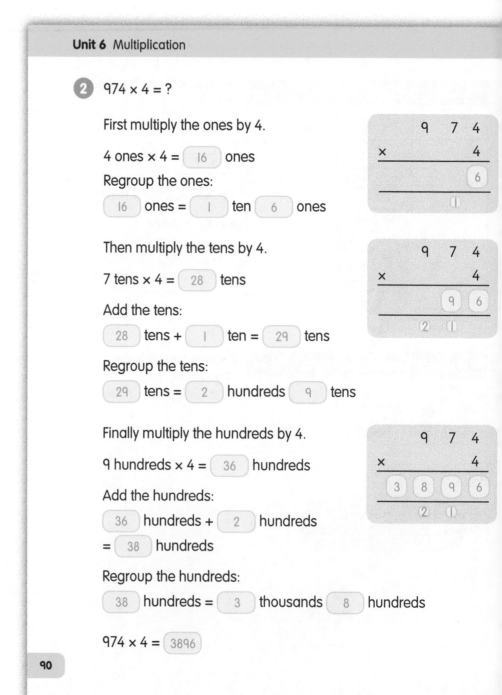

Unit 6 Multiplication

2 974 × 4 = ?

First multiply the ones by 4.

4 ones × 4 = (16) ones

Regroup the ones:

(16) ones = (1) ten (6) ones

Then multiply the tens by 4.

7 tens × 4 = (28) tens

Add the tens:

(28) tens + (1) ten = (29) tens

Regroup the tens:

(29) tens = (2) hundreds (9) tens

Finally multiply the hundreds by 4.

9 hundreds × 4 = (36) hundreds

Add the hundreds:

(36) hundreds + (2) hundreds

= (38) hundreds

Regroup the hundreds:

(38) hundreds = (3) thousands (8) hundreds

974 × 4 = (3896)

90

③ Multiply.

a
```
    4 5 8
  ×     4
```
⎧ 1 ⎫⎧ 8 ⎫⎧ 3 ⎫⎧ 2 ⎫
      ② ③

b
```
    5 7 6
  ×     2
```
⎧ 1 ⎫⎧ 1 ⎫⎧ 5 ⎫⎧ 2 ⎫
        ① ①

c
```
  3 4 5
×     3
```
⎧ 1035 ⎫

d
```
  2 9 8
×     5
```
⎧ 1490 ⎫

Practice Book 3B, p.31 and 33

Let's Explore!

④ Look at the four digits below.

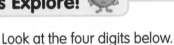

Use the digits to make multiplication sentences that give:

a the greatest product

b the smallest product.

(4)(3)(2) × (5) = ⎧ 2160 ⎫

(3)(4)(5) × (2) = ⎧ 690 ⎫

Greatest product

(4)(3)(2)

×   (5)
_____
⎧ 2 1 6 0 ⎫

Smallest product

(3)(4)(5)

×   (2)
_____
⎧ 6 9 0 ⎫

91

- Pupils should work on this exercise individually. Ensure that they have already mastered the 2, 3, 4 and 5 times tables.

④ *Let's Explore!*

- In this activity, some pupils may resort to the 'guess and check' method. Encourage them to use deduction to determine the smallest and greatest value.

Independent work

Practice 4, Practice 5 and *Maths Journal* in Practice Book 3B, pp 31 to 36.

Objective of activity

Pupils will be able to apply the 'guess and check' and deduction strategies to find the greatest and the smallest product by multiplying a 1-digit number and a 3-digit number with regrouping.

Objective of activity

Pupils will be able to apply the 'using pattern' strategy and the multiplication concept to find the sum of a set of consecutive numbers.

Thinking skills

Applying the pattern strategy and seeing connections between numbers

Independent work

Challenging Practice and *Problem Solving* in Practice Book 3B, pp 37 to 38.

Teaching sequence

5 *Put On Your Thinking Caps!*

- List pairs of numbers that add up to 10:
  1 + 9, 2 + 8, 3 + 7, 4 + 6
- Since there are four sets of numbers, they make 4 groups of 10s.
  Sum of eight numbers = 4 × 10
  = 40

6

- Encourage pupils to look for pairs of numbers that have the same sum.
- In this case, the sum is 11, 2 + 9, 3 + 8, 4 + 7, 5 + 6. Four sets of 11 is 44.

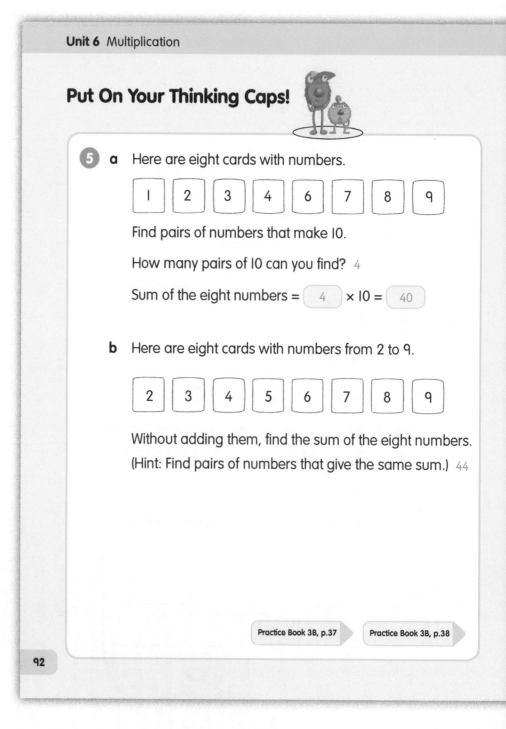

Unit 6 Multiplication

Put On Your Thinking Caps!

5 a Here are eight cards with numbers.

| 1 | 2 | 3 | 4 | 6 | 7 | 8 | 9 |

Find pairs of numbers that make 10.

How many pairs of 10 can you find? 4

Sum of the eight numbers = 4 × 10 = 40

b Here are eight cards with numbers from 2 to 9.

| 2 | 3 | 4 | 5 | 6 | 7 | 8 | 9 |

Without adding them, find the sum of the eight numbers. (Hint: Find pairs of numbers that give the same sum.) 44

Practice Book 3B, p.37   Practice Book 3B, p.38

92

Unit 6 Multiplication

Date: _____

Practice 1   Multiplication without regrouping

1 Multiply and fill in the boxes.

a

```
  1 3
×   2
─────
  2 6
```

3 ones × 2 = 6 ones

1 ten × 2 = 2 tens

b

```
  3 4 2
×     2
───────
  6 8 4
```

2 ones × 2 = 4 ones

4 tens × 2 = 8 tens

3 hundreds × 2 = 6 hundreds

c   312 × 3 = ?

2 ones × 3 = 6 ones

1 ten × 3 = 3 tens

3 hundreds × 3 = 9 hundreds

312 × 3 = 9 hundreds 3 tens 6 ones

= 936

23

Unit 6: Multiplication

Answers Unit 6: Multiplication   161

2 Answer these questions.

a
```
  4 1 4
×     2
-------
  8 2 8
```

b
```
  3 2 1
×     3
-------
  9 6 3
```

c
```
  1 0 2
×     4
-------
  4 0 8
```

d
```
  1 0 1
×     5
-------
  5 0 5
```

3 Match the caterpillar to the correct leaf.

646 — 201 × 3

408 — 323 × 2

603 — 222 × 4

888 — 102 × 4

4 The hungry frog is hunting flies.
The flies that show a product of more than 400 are the tastiest.
Which flies should the frog eat?

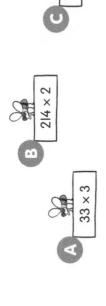
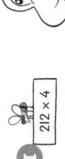
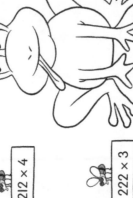

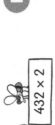

A 33 × 3

B 214 × 2

C 123 × 3

D 111 × 5

E 144 × 2

F 122 × 4

G 432 × 2

H 222 × 3

I 212 × 4

The frog should eat flies **B,** D, F, G, H, I

Practice 2 | Multiplication with regrouping in ones, tens and hundreds

1 Multiply and fill in the spaces and boxes.

a $18 \times 7 = ?$

T	O
1	8
×	7

[1] [2] (5) [6]

Follow these steps to multiply.

First multiply the ones by 7.

8 ones × 7 = 56 ones

56 ones = 5 tens 6 ones   Regroup the ones.

Then multiply the tens by 7.

1 ten × 7 = 7 tens

Add the tens.

7 tens + 5 tens = 12 tens

12 tens = 1 hundred 2 tens   Regroup the tens.

18 × 7 = 1 hundred 2 tens 6 ones

= 126

5 Multiply.

a Ruby picks 22 plums each day.
How many plums does she pick in 4 days?

22 × 4 = 88
She picks 88 plums in 4 days.

b Miss Smith prints 143 newsletters every month.
How many newsletters does she print in 2 months?

143 × 2 = 286
She prints 286 newsletters in 2 months.

c The postman delivered 232 letters yesterday.
Today he delivered the same number of letters.
How many letters did he deliver in total?

232 × 2 = 464
He delivered 464 letters in total.

b 145 × 4 = ?

$$
\begin{array}{ccc}
H & T & O \\
1 & 4 & 5 \\
\times & & 4 \\
\hline
5 & 8 & 0 \\
& ① & ②
\end{array}
$$

Follow these steps to multiply.

First multiply the ones by 4.

5 ones × 4 = __20__ ones

__20__ ones = __2__ tens 0 ones   `Regroup the ones.`

Then multiply the tens by 4.

__4__ tens × 4 = __16__ tens

Next add the tens.

__16__ tens + __2__ tens = __18__ tens

__18__ tens = __1__ hundred 8 tens   `Regroup the tens.`

Then multiply the hundreds by 4.

__1__ hundred × 4 = __4__ hundreds

Add the hundreds.

__4__ hundreds + __1__ hundred = __5__ hundreds

145 × 4 = __5__ hundreds __8__ tens __0__ ones

= __580__

Date: _____

| Practice 3 | Multiplication with regrouping in ones, tens and hundreds |

1 Which key can't unlock the treasure chests? Multiply.

35 × 5 → 175 **(K)**

486 × 2 → 972 **(D)**

279 × 3 → 837 **(Y)**

297 × 3 → 891 **(A)**

304 × 3 → 912 **(L)**

156 × 4 → 624 **(O)**

174 × 4 → 696 **(U)**

196 × 4 → 784 **(S)**

238 × 4 → 952 **(M)**

248 × 4 → 992 **(N)**

155 × 5 → 775 **(Z)**

199 × 5 → 995 **(E)**

Write the letters that match the answers.

D	O	N	K	E	Y
972	624	992	175	995	837

Practice 4 — Multiplication with regrouping in ones, tens, hundreds and thousands

1 $349 \times 5 = ?$

Follow these steps to multiply.

Th	H	T	O
	3	4	9
×			5
1	7	4	5
	②	④	

First multiply the ones by 5.

9 ones × 5 = 45 ones

45 ones = 4 tens 5 ones   **Regroup the ones.**

Then multiply the tens by 5.

4 tens × 5 = 20 tens

Add the tens.

20 tens + 4 tens = 24 tens

24 tens = 2 hundreds 4 tens   **Regroup the tens.**

Finally multiply the hundreds by 5.

3 hundreds × 5 = 15 hundreds

Add the hundreds.

15 hundreds + 2 hundreds = 17 hundreds

17 hundreds = 1 thousand 7 hundreds   **Regroup the hundreds.**

349 × 5 = 1 thousand 7 hundreds 4 tens 5 ones

= 1745

2 Solve these word problems.

a A factory makes 84 carpets in a year.
How many carpets does the factory make in 5 years?

84 × 5 = 420
The factory makes 420 carpets in 5 years.

b There are 187 cars in a car park.
Each car has 4 wheels.
How many wheels are there altogether?

187 × 4 = 748
There are 748 wheels altogether.

c There are 198 children in a school.
Each child gives 4 books to charity.
How many books do they give to charity altogether?

198 × 4 = 792
They give 792 books to charity altogether.

d Ruby feeds her rabbit 5 green beans each day.
How many green beans does the rabbit eat in 165 days?

165 × 5 = 825
The rabbit eats 825 green beans in 165 days.

Date: _____

Practice 5

Multiplication with regrouping in ones, tens, hundreds and thousands

1 Solve these word problems.

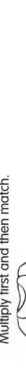

a Tai has 3 boxes of cubes.
Each box contains 484 cubes.
How many cubes does Tai have altogether?

$484 \times 3 = 1452$
Tai has 1452 cubes altogether.

b A supermarket donates £622 to charity.
Three other supermarkets and a newsagent each donate the same amount of money.
How much money do they donate altogether?

$£622 \times 5 = £3110$
They donate £3110 altogether.

2 The children are going to a fancy dress party!
Help them to match the tops with the hats.
Multiply first and then match.

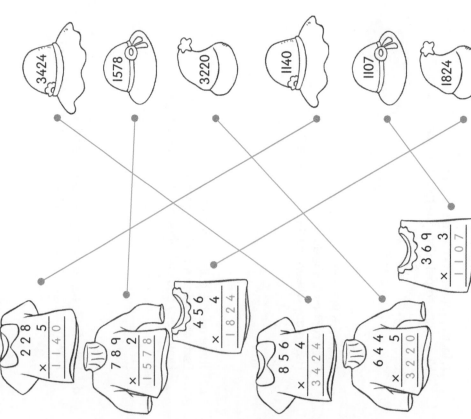

Hats: 3424, 1578, 3220, 1140, 1107, 1824

Tops:
228 × 5 = 1140
789 × 2 = 1578
456 × 4 = 1824
856 × 4 = 3424
644 × 5 = 3220
369 × 3 = 1107

c Miya and her 3 friends each have 536 beads.
How many beads do they have altogether?

536 × 4 = 2144
They have 2144 beads altogether.

d A shopkeeper buys 148 packets of football stickers.
Each packet contains 9 stickers.
How many football stickers does he buy altogether?

148 × 9 = 1332
He buys 1332 football stickers altogether.

---

2 Isabel and her friends take part in a treasure hunt.
To win, they need clues from the correct treasure chests.
Find the correct chests by answering the questions below.
Fill in the spaces and then colour the correct chests.

a Which of these pairs gives the greatest product?

213 × 3 = 639

150 × 6 = 900

432 × 4 = 1728

639   900   1728   1900

b The product of 854 and 9 is 7686.

7868   7688   7686   7866

c Rosa runs from Tree A to B to C, to D to E, and then to F.
The trees are 934 m apart from each other.
How far does Rosa run altogether?

Rosa runs 4670 m.

4560   4670   4760   4650

Maths Journal

Date: _____

1 Tai wants to multiply 243 by 2.
This is how he works it out.

Step 1: Multiply 3 ones by 2.
3 ones × 2 = 6 ones

```
  2 4 3
×     2
-------
      6
```

Step 2: Multiply 4 tens by 2.
4 tens × 2 = 8 tens

```
  2 4 3
×     2
-------
    8 6
```

Step 3: Multiply 2 hundreds by 2.
2 hundreds × 2 = 4 hundreds

```
  2 4 3
×     2
-------
  4 8 6
```

Now you try it.
Multiply 323 by 3.

```
  3 2 3
×     3
-------
  9 6 9
```

Write down the steps to get the answer.

Step 1: Multiply 3 ones by 3.
3 ones × 3 = 9 ones

Step 2: Multiply 2 tens by 3.
2 tens × 3 = 6 tens

Step 3: Multiply 3 hundreds by 3.
3 hundreds × 3 = 9 hundreds

Challenging Practice

Date: _____

1 Fill in the missing numbers.

a
```
  2 [4]
×   2
-----
  4 8
```

b
```
  1 1 [1]
×     [5]
-------
  5 5 5
```

c
```
  1 [3] 5
×       4
-------
  5 4 0
```

d
```
  [2] 5 2
×       3
-------
  7 5 6
```

Review 3

Date: _____

1 Fill in the spaces.

a 6 + 6 + 6 = __18__   b 9 sixes = 9 × __6__

c 4 × 7 = __4__ sevens   d 7 × 6 = 6 × __7__

e 8 + 8 + 8 + 8 + 8 = 5 × __8__

f 5 nines + 3 nines = __8__ × 9

g 9 + 9 + 9 + 9 + 9 = __5__ nines

2 Skip-count and fill in the circles.

a Skip-count in sixes.

(6) (12) (18) (24) (30) (36) (42) (48) (54) (60)
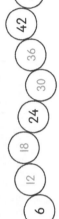

b Skip-count in sevens.

(7) (14) (21) (28) (35) (42) (49) (56) (63) (70)

Date: _____

Problem Solving

1 Farmer Jones has 100 geese and sheep on his farm.
They have a total of 340 legs.
How many of each type of animals does Farmer Jones have?

Geese (2 legs)	Sheep (4 legs)	Total number of legs	Correct (✓) or Not correct (✗)
50 × 2 = 100	50 × 4 = 200	100 + 200 = 300	✗
60 × 2 = 120	40 × 4 = 160	120 + 160 = 280	✗
30 × 2 = 60	70 × 4 = 280	60 + 280 = 340	✓

Farmer Jones has __30__ geese and __70__ sheep.

c Skip-count in eights.

8 16 24 32 40 48 56 64 72 80

d Skip-count in nines.

9 18 27 36 45 54 63 72 81 90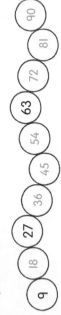

3 Multiply.

a 5 × 7 = 35
6 × 7 = 35 + 7
= 42

b 10 × 9 = 90
8 × 9 = 90 − 9 − 9
= 72

4 Multiply.

a
```
  2 3 2
×     2
  4 6 4
```

b
```
  4 0 3
×     3
1 2 0 9
```

c
```
  2 8 0
×     4
1 1 2 0
```

d
```
  7 0 9
×     5
3 5 4 5
```

e
```
  2 6 9
×     3
  8 0 7
```

f
```
  5 3 9
×     5
2 6 9 5
```

5 Fill in the spaces.

a 5 × 4 = 20
20 ÷ 4 = 5
20 ÷ 5 = 4

b 6 × 3 = 18
18 ÷ 3 = 6
18 ÷ 6 = 3

6 The baker has 120 kg of flour.
He packs the flour into bags of 5 kg.
How many bags does he need?

120 ÷ 5 = 24
He needs 24 bags.

7 Hardeep buys 6 packets of football stickers.
Each packet contains 12 football stickers.
How many football stickers does he buy altogether?

12 × 6 = 72
He buys 72 football stickers altogether.

8 Millie does 15 pages of maths questions.
There are 9 questions on each page.
How many questions does she do altogether?

$15 \times 9 = 135$
She does 135 questions altogether.

9 Peter has 48 marbles.
He packs all the marbles into bags of 8 marbles each.
How many bags of marbles are there?

$48 \div 8 = 6$
There are 6 bags of marbles.

10 Farmer Brown delivers 250 eggs to 5 shops.
Each shop gets an equal number of eggs.
How many eggs does each shop get?

$250 \div 5 = 50$
Each shop gets 50 eggs.

Review 3

42

Week	Learning Objectives	Thinking Skills	Resources
4	**(1) Quotient and remainder** Pupils will be able to: • divide a 1-digit or a 2-digit number by a 1-digit number without remainder • divide a 1-digit or a 2-digit number by a 1-digit number with remainder • apply the multiplication facts strategy to find the quotient in division with remainder • use the long division format to divide and find the quotient and remainder • associate 'quotient' and 'remainder' with division	• Identifying relationships • Recalling and relating multiplication and division facts	• Pupil Textbook 3A, pp 93 to 96 • Practice Book 3B, pp 43 to 44 • Teacher's Guide 3A, pp 175 to 178
4	**(2) Odd and even numbers** Pupils will be able to: • use pattern with concrete representations to identify and name 'odd' and 'even' numbers • use division by 2 to determine whether a number is even or odd • use the fact that all odd numbers end with 1, 3, 5, 7 or 9 while all even numbers end with 2, 4, 6, 8 or 0	• Classifying • Identifying relationships • Relating number facts	• Pupil Textbook 3A, pp 97 to 98 • Practice Book 3B, pp 45 to 46 • Teacher's Guide 3A, pp 179 to 180

Week	Learning Objectives	Thinking Skills	Resources
4	**(3) Division without remainder and regrouping** Pupils will be able to: • show, with concrete representations in a place value chart, a number divided by another number with no regrouping or remainder • divide a 2-digit number by a 1-digit number with no regrouping or remainder • carry out the procedures in division starting with tens and followed by ones	• Classifying • Identifying relationships • Recalling and relating multiplication and division facts	• Pupil Textbook 3A, pp 99 to 100 • Practice Book 3B, pp 47 to 48 • Teacher's Guide 3A, pp 181 to 182
4	**(4) Division with regrouping in tens and ones** Pupils will be able to: • use concrete representations to show regrouping from tens to ones in division • show division of a 2-digit number by a 1-digit number with regrouping from tens to ones, with or without remainder • carry out the procedures in division starting from tens with regrouping, followed by ones • solve simple division word problems involving division of a 2-digit number by a 1-digit number with regrouping from tens to ones	• Classifying • Identifying relationships • Recalling and relating multiplication and division facts	• Pupil Textbook 3A, pp 101 to 103 • Practice Book 3B, pp 49 to 50 • Teacher's Guide 3A, pp 183 to 185

Week	Learning Objectives	Thinking Skills	Resources
5	**(5) Division with regrouping in hundreds, tens and ones** Pupils will be able to: • use concrete representations in a place value chart to show regrouping from hundreds to tens, then from tens to ones in division • divide a 3-digit number by a 1-digit number with regrouping from hundreds to tens, then from tens to ones with or without remainder • carry out the procedures in division starting from tens with regrouping and followed by ones • solve simple word problems involving division of a 3-digit number by a 1-digit number with regrouping from hundreds to tens, then from tens to ones with or without remainder *Let's Explore!* Pupils will be able to: • discover a pattern in a magic square • explore whether or not adding, subtracting, multiplying or dividing a number will produce the same pattern	• Associating • Identifying relationships • Recalling and relating multiplication and division facts Heuristic for problem solving: • Looking for patterns	• Pupil Textbook 3A, pp 104 to 109 • Practice Book 3B, pp 51 to 54 • Teacher's Guide 3A, pp 186 to 191
5	*Put On Your Thinking Caps!* Pupils will be able to use deduction to find unknown values to solve problems in long division. *Maths Journal* Pupils will be able to reflect on the division procedures to check if the given methods are correct.	• Associating • Identifying relationships • Relating multiplication and division facts	• Pupil Textbook 3A, p 110 • Practice Book 3B, pp 55 to 58 • Teacher's Guide 3A, p 192

Summative assessment opportunity

Assessment Book 3, Test 3, pp 25 to 30

Division

Learning objectives:
Quotient and remainder

Pupils will be able to:

- divide a 1-digit or a 2-digit number by a 1-digit number without remainder

- divide a 1-digit or a 2-digit number by a 1-digit number with remainder

- apply the multiplication facts strategy to find the quotient in division with remainder

- use the long division format to divide and find the quotient and remainder

- associate 'quotient' and 'remainder' with division

Key concept

Division of a 2-digit number by a 1-digit number with remainder

---

Unit 7 Division

Let's Learn!

Quotient and remainder

1 Ella and Tai are at the beach collecting seashells and pebbles.
They divide 8 buckets equally between them.
   a   How many buckets does each child get?
   b   How many buckets are left?

a   8 ÷ 2 = ?

8 ones ÷ 2 = 4 ones with no remainder
Quotient = 4 ones
Remainder = 0 ones

$$\begin{array}{r} 4 \\ 2\overline{)8} \\ 8 \\ \hline 0 \end{array}$$

Each child gets 4 buckets.

b   There are no buckets left.

93

Teaching sequence

1

- Read out and explain the question. Guide pupils to relate the division concept to 8 divided by 2.
8 buckets ÷ 2 = ____ buckets each

- Explain the strategy to divide 8 buckets equally between 2 children. Guide pupils to use the multiplication fact to find the division fact.

- Introduce another strategy using long division:
8 ones ÷ 2 = 4 ones with no remainder.

- Show the following working in vertical format:

$$\begin{array}{r} 4 \\ 2\overline{)8} \\ 8 \\ \hline 0 \end{array}$$

Quotient

We divide exactly by 2. There is no remainder

- Explain the term **quotient**, which refers to the number of items each group will contain.

- Identifying relationships
- Recalling and relating
  multiplication and division facts

Teaching sequence

- Read the question to the class. Encourage pupils to interpret the picture and to relate it to the relevant information in the question.
- Guide pupils to link the picture to division of the number of shells, i.e., 11 seashells shared among 4 children.

  $11 \div 4 =$ _____

  Show the long division for 11 divided by 4.

- Explain the strategy to find the quotient. Recall two or more multiplication facts and select the multiplication fact that gives the correct quotient. (Refer to the thought bubble in the textbook.)

- Explain the results of division. What is the quotient and what does it represent? What is the remainder and what does it represent?

Unit 7 Division

2 4 children share 11 seashells equally between them.

a How many seashells does each child get?
b How many seashells are left?

a 11 ÷ 4 = ?

Divide the 11 seashells into 4 equal groups.

4 × **2** = 8
8 is less than 11.
4 × **3** = 12
12 is more than 11.
Choose 2.

11 ones ÷ 4 = 2 ones with remainder 3 ones
            = 2 r 3
Quotient   = 2 ones
Remainder = 3 ones

Each child gets 2 seashells.

b 3 seashells are left.

Remember, 'r' stands for remainder.

$$\begin{array}{r} 2\ \text{r}3 \\ 4\overline{)11} \\ \underline{8} \\ 3 \end{array}$$

94

Additional activity

Show the following division to
pupils:

$$3\overline{)14}$$ with 4 above and 12 subtracted leaving 2

Ask them to write a simple word
problem based on this division.

3 3 children share 17 pebbles equally between them.

a How many pebbles does each child get?

b How many pebbles are left?

a 17 ÷ 3 = ?

$$3\overline{)17}$$ with $5\,r\,2$ above and 15 subtracted leaving 2

3 × **5** = 15
15 is less than 17.
3 × **6** = 18
18 is more than 17.
Choose 5.

17 ones ÷ 3 = 5 ones with remainder 2 ones

= (5) r (2)

Quotient = (5) ones

Remainder = (2) ones

Each child gets (5) pebbles.

b (2) pebbles are left.

4 Find the missing numbers.

a 20 ones ÷ 3 = (6) r (2)   **b** 43 ones ÷ 5 = (8) r (3)

Quotient = (6) ones   Quotient = (8) ones

Remainder = (2) ones   Remainder = (3) ones

95

Teaching sequence

- Ask pupils to work in pairs.
Ask them to read the question
and guide them to interpret
the requirement of the
question. Pupils should work
together to use long division
to find the quotient and the
remainder. Pupils should
then interpret and answer the
question using the values of
the quotient and remainder.

- Pupils should work individually
or in pairs to complete the
divisions.

Thinking skills

- Recalling
- Relating multiplication facts to concepts in division

What you will need

- Interlocking cubes (50 cubes per group)
- Number cards from 10 to 50
- Spinner with numbers 2, 3, 4 and 5

Independent work

Practice 1 in Practice Book 3B, pp 43 to 44.

Teaching sequence

5 *Game*

- This activity helps pupils to understand division with remainders, using some concrete representations. It also helps to strengthen the use of multiplication facts for division.

Unit 7 Division

Game

5 **Find the remainder!**

How to play:

Players: 2 to 4
You will need:
- cubes
- number cards from 10 to 50
- spinner with numbers 2, 3, 4 and 5

1 Shuffle the number cards. Pick a card to get a number.

2 Select the number of cubes shown on the card. For example, for the number card 32:
- select 32 cubes
- arrange them in tens and ones.
You will have 3 tens and 2 ones.

3 Spin the spinner to get another number.

4 Divide the cubes by the number shown on the spinner, and find the remainder. For example, if the pointer points to 5:
- rearrange the 32 cubes into 5 equal groups
- count the cubes in each group and the remaining cubes.
You will have 2 remaining cubes.

5 The other players check the answer using division.

```
      6
 5 ) 3 2
     3 0
     ───
       2
```

6 Take turns to play. Play two rounds each.

96   The player with the most correct answers wins!   Practice Book 3B, p.43

Learning objectives:
Odd and even numbers

Pupils will be able to:

- use pattern with concrete representations to identify and name 'odd and even' numbers
- use division by 2 to determine whether a number is even or odd
- use the fact that all odd numbers end with 1, 3, 5, 7 or 9 while all even numbers end with 2, 4, 6, 8 or 0

Key concept

Recognising patterns to identify odd and even numbers

Thinking skills

- Classifying
- Identifying relationships
- Relating number facts

What you will need

Interlocking cubes

Teaching sequence

1

- Demonstrate, using cubes, what an odd number is. Use cubes to make the pattern in the textbook.
- Ask pupils to look at the pattern and explain how it is made using cubes corresponding to the sets of numbers 1, 3, 5, 7 and 9.
- Explain the pattern: in each set, the yellow cubes make pairs while the red cube is left out. The numbers that provide this pattern are the **odd numbers**. So 1, 3, 5, 7 and 9 are odd numbers.

2

- Use cubes to make the pattern using numbers 2, 4, 6, 8 and 10 as shown in the textbook.
- Encourage pupils to observe and explain how the pattern is made with cubes corresponding to the set of numbers 2, 4, 6, 8 and 10.
- Explain the pattern: in each set, two cubes are linked and each one has a partner. The numbers that provide this pattern are the **even numbers**.
- Explain how this pattern is different from the pattern made by the previous set.
- Summarise the following: numbers ending with 0, 2, 4, 6 or 8 are even numbers. Numbers ending with 1, 3, 5, 7 or 9 are odd numbers.

Division **Unit 7**

Let's Learn!

Odd and even numbers

1 1, 3, 5, 7 and 9 cubes were used to make the following patterns.

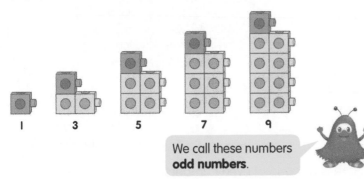

1	3	5	7	9

> We call these numbers **odd numbers**.

Odd numbers are numbers in which the ones digit is 1, 3, 5, 7 or 9. Name some odd numbers.

2 These patterns were made using 2, 4, 6, 8 and 10 cubes.

> We call these numbers **even numbers**. 0 is also an even number.

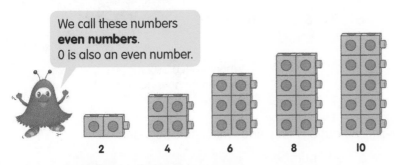

2	4	6	8	10

Even numbers are numbers in which the ones digit is 2, 4, 6, 8 or 0. Name some even numbers.

97

Unit 7: Division **179**

Additional activity

Provide pupils with some cubes. Ask them to make a set of odd numbers and another set of even numbers with the cubes. Ask them to write down the set of odd and even numbers.

Teaching sequence

- Explain the strategy of using division by 2 to determine whether a given number is odd.
- Demonstrate dividing 13 by 2, which gives a remainder of 1. Explain that 13 is an odd number as there is a remainder.
- Ask pupils to work on the next two questions to divide the given odd numbers by 2. Guide pupils to see that odd numbers, when divided by 2, always have a remainder.

- Explain the strategy of using division by 2 to determine whether a given number is even. Demonstrate dividing 12 by 2, which has no remainder. Explain that 12 is an even number as there is no remainder.
- Ask pupils to work on the next two questions to divide the given even numbers by 2. Guide pupils to see that even numbers, when divided by 2, never have a remainder.

- Summarise the two strategies to determine whether a given number is even or odd:
  1) Even numbers always end with 2, 4, 6, 8 or 0. Odd numbers always end with 1, 3, 5, 7 or 9.
  2) When a number is divided by 2 and has no remainder, the number is even. When a number is divided by 2 and has a remainder, the number is odd.
- Ask pupils to work on the questions in this section, using one of the strategies given above.

Unit 7 Division

3 Look at this group of odd numbers.

| ODD |
| 13   17   19 |

Divide each number by 2. What do you notice?

Example

$$2\overline{)13} \quad \begin{array}{r} 6\ r1 \\ 1\ 2 \\ \hline 1 \end{array}$$

6 × 2 = 12. 12 is less than 13.
7 × 2 = 14. 14 is more than 13.
Choose 6 as the quotient.

a $2\overline{)17}$ b $2\overline{)19}$
    8 r1   9 r1

When divided by 2, an odd number always has a remainder.

4 Here is a group of even numbers.

| EVEN |
| 12   16   20 |

Divide each number by 2. What do you notice?

Example

$$2\overline{)12} \quad \begin{array}{r} 6 \\ 1\ 2 \\ \hline 0 \end{array}$$

6 × 2 = 12

a $2\overline{)16}$ b $2\overline{)20}$
    8 r0   10 r0

When divided by 2, an even number never has a remainder!

5 Without dividing, find which numbers are:

a odd numbers
   17, 77 and 129
b even numbers.
   8, 26 and 38

    8   17   26   38   77   129

Practice Book 3B, p.45

98

Learning objectives: Division without remainder and regrouping

Pupils will be able to:

- show, with concrete representations in a place value chart, a number divided by another number with no regrouping or remainder
- divide a 2-digit number by a I-digit number with no regrouping or remainder
- carry out the procedures in division starting with tens and followed by ones

Key concepts

- Expressing a number as a sum of values of different places
- Dividing equally with no remainder

Thinking skills

- Classifying
- Identifying relationships
- Recalling and relating multiplication and division facts

Division **Unit 7**

Let's Learn!

Division without remainder and regrouping

1 Ella, Peter and Ruby are collecting twigs and acorns in the garden.

They share 63 twigs equally between them.
How many twigs does each child get?

$63 \div 3 = ?$

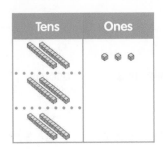

First divide the **tens** by 3.
6 tens ÷ 3 = 2 tens

$$\begin{array}{r} 2 \\ 3\overline{)6\ 3} \\ 6 \end{array}$$

99

Teaching sequence

1

- Explain to pupils that to share 63 twigs between 3 children, we have to write 63 as a sum of values that make tens and ones. Show this with a place value chart:
  63 = 6 tens 3 ones

- Physically divide 6 tens into 3 groups of 2 tens and 3 ones into 3 groups of I one.

- Show the following using cubes on place value charts, and then followed by long division.

  First divide the **tens** by 3.
  6 tens ÷ 3 = 2 tens

  Then divide the **ones** by 3.
  3 ones ÷ 3 = I one

  There are 2 tens and I one in each group.
  63 ÷ 3 = 2I

- Show the following working in vertical format, emphasising the given place value of each digit:

$$\begin{array}{r} 2I \\ 3\ \overline{)\ 63} \\ 6 \\ \hline 3 \\ 3 \\ \hline 0 \end{array}$$

Independent work

Practice 3 in Practice Book 3B, pp 47 to 48.

Additional activity

Ask pupils to work in pairs. Ask them to each write two division questions similar to ③ and work out the answers. They should rub out the tens or ones digit of the dividend of the questions. Their partner will then find out what the missing numbers are.

Teaching sequence

- Ask pupils to work in pairs using base ten equipment in place value charts to represent
  39 acorns divided equally between 3 children.
- Ask them to use the same procedure in ① to carry out the division. The following summarises the procedure.
  1. First write 39 as 3 tens and 9 ones.
  2. Show sharing of 3 tens 9 ones between 3 groups as follows:
     3 tens ÷ 3 = 1 ten
  3. Then divide the **ones** by 3:
     9 ones ÷ 3 = 3 ones
  4. There are 1 ten 3 ones in each group.
     39 ÷ 3 = 13
- Show the workings in vertical format.

- Ask pupils to attempt these problems in vertical format.

Unit 7 Division

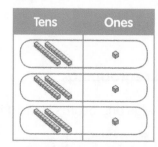

Then divide the **ones** by 3.
3 ones ÷ 3 = 1 one

$$3\overline{)63}$$

So 63 ÷ 3 = 21.

Each child gets 21 twigs.

② The children share 39 acorns equally between them. How many acorns does each child get?

39 ÷ 3 = ?

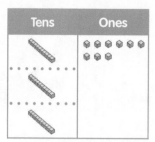

First divide the **tens** by 3.

3 tens ÷ 3 = [1] ten

$$3\overline{)39}$$

Then divide the **ones** by 3.

9 ones ÷ 3 = [3] ones

$$3\overline{)39}$$

So 39 ÷ 3 = [13].

Each child gets [13] acorns.

③ Divide.

a $4\overline{)48}$ b $5\overline{)55}$ c $2\overline{)64}$ d $3\overline{)93}$

100

Practice Book 3B, p.47

Learning objectives: Division with regrouping in tens and ones

Pupils will be able to:

- use concrete representations to show regrouping from tens to ones in division
- show division of a 2-digit number by a 1-digit number with regrouping from tens to ones, with or without remainder
- carry out the procedures in division starting from tens with regrouping, followed by ones
- solve simple division word problems involving division of a 2-digit number by a 1-digit number with regrouping from tens to ones

Key concepts

- Expressing a number as a sum of values of different places
- Dividing equally with or without remainder
- Regrouping from values of a higher place (tens) to a lower place (ones) in division

Thinking skills

- Classifying
- Identifying relationships
- Recalling and relating multiplication and division facts

Teaching sequence

1

- Explain to pupils that to share 52 cards between Peter and Miya, we have to write 52 as a sum of values that makes tens and ones. Demonstrate this with a place value chart:

    52 = 5 tens 2 ones

  Show 5 tens and 2 ones using base ten equipment in a place value chart. Demonstrate with concrete representations that 5 tens has to be regrouped so that it can be shared. How many tens will each one get?

  5 tens = 4 tens + 1 ten
          = 4 tens + 10 ones
  So 5 tens 2 ones = 4 tens + 10 ones + 2 ones = 4 tens 12 ones.

  Demonstrate the division below using base ten equipment in a place value chart, and then with long division.

  First divide the **tens** by 2.
  5 tens ÷ 2 = 2 tens with remainder 1 ten = 2 tens 10 ones (**Regroup** the remainder 1 ten: 1 ten for 10 ones)

  Add the ones:
  10 ones + 2 ones = 12 ones

  Then divide the **ones** by 2.
  12 ones ÷ 2 = 6 ones. There are 2 tens 6 ones in each group.
  52 ÷ 2 = 26

- Show the working in vertical format. Emphasise to pupils the importance of correct placement of each digit in the vertical working.

Let's Learn!

Division with regrouping in tens and ones

1 Peter and Miya are playing cards.
They share 52 cards equally between them.
How many cards does each child get?

52 ÷ 2 = ?

Tens	Ones

First divide the **tens** by 2.
5 tens ÷ 2
= 2 tens with remainder 1 ten

$$\begin{array}{r} 2 \\ 2\overline{)5\,2} \\ 4 \\ \hline 1 \end{array}$$

Tens	Ones

Regroup the remainder ten:
1 ten = 10 ones

Add the ones:
10 ones + 2 ones = 12 ones

$$\begin{array}{r} 2 \\ 2\overline{)5\,2} \\ 4 \\ \hline 1\,2 \end{array}$$

Tens	Ones

Then divide the **ones** by 2.
12 ones ÷ 2 = 6 ones

So 52 ÷ 2 = 26.

Each child gets 26 cards.

$$\begin{array}{r} 2\,6 \\ 2\overline{)5\,2} \\ 4 \\ \hline 1\,2 \\ 1\,2 \\ \hline 0 \end{array}$$

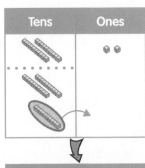

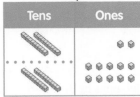

101

Additional activity

Ask pupils to work in groups. Give each group some base ten equipment or counters. Ask them to practise regrouping using these concrete representations.

E.g., 43 = _____ tens 13 ones

72 = _____ tens 12 ones

Teaching sequence

- Ask pupils to work in pairs to find 76 ÷ 3.
- Provide pupils with base ten equipment to help them visualise the regrouping process. If necessary, show the following processes in regrouping using base ten equipment.

76 = 7 tens + 6 ones
  = 6 tens 1 ten + 6 ones
  = 6 tens 10 ones + 6 ones
  = 6 tens + 16 ones

Unit 7 Division

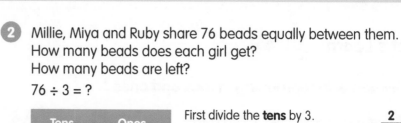

② Millie, Miya and Ruby share 76 beads equally between them. How many beads does each girl get? How many beads are left?

76 ÷ 3 = ?

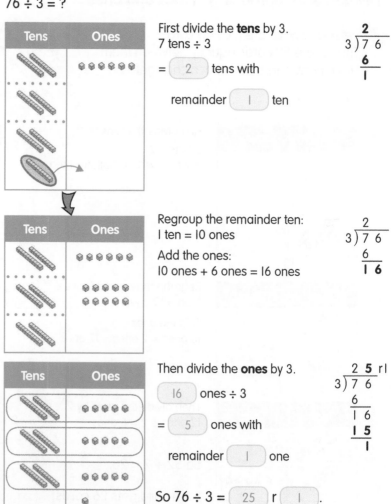

First divide the **tens** by 3.
7 tens ÷ 3

= (2) tens with

remainder (1) ten

$$3\overline{)76}$$
  6
  ─
  1

Regroup the remainder ten:
1 ten = 10 ones
Add the ones:
10 ones + 6 ones = 16 ones

  2
$$3\overline{)76}$$
  6
  ──
  1 6

Then divide the **ones** by 3.
(16) ones ÷ 3

= (5) ones with

remainder (1) one

So 76 ÷ 3 = (25) r (1).

   2 **5** r1
$$3\overline{)76}$$
   6
   ──
   1 6
   1 5
   ──
   1

Each girl gets (25) beads. (1) bead is left.

102

Independent work

Practice 4 in Practice Book 3B, pp 49 to 50.

Additional activity

Ask pupils to work in pairs. Ask them to find the missing numbers for the following:

(1)
```
    □□
5 ) 6 5
    5
    ┌─┐
  1 │□│
    └─┘
  1 │□│
    └─┘
    │□│
    └─┘
```

(2)
```
    □□
4 ) 5 3
    4
    ┌─┐
  1 │□│
    └─┘
  1 │□│
    └─┘
    │□│
    └─┘
```

Activity

3 Use base ten equipment to help you divide.

Here's a hint. Regroup each remainder ten into 10 ones.

a Divide 7 tens 2 ones between 2 children.

b Divide 5 tens and 7 ones into 3 baskets.

c Divide 9 tens and 6 ones among 4 families.

4 Divide.

a $4\overline{)5\,6}$ 14

b $5\overline{)7\,5}$ 15

c $2\overline{)7\,9}$ 39 r1

d $3\overline{)8\,6}$ 28 r2

5 Tai has 48 apples.
He puts them equally into 4 bags.
How many apples are in each bag? 12 apples

6 Ruby divides 63 marbles into bags of 5 marbles each.
How many bags did she get? 12 bags
How many marbles are left? 3 marbles

Practice Book 3B, p.49

103

Teaching sequence

3

- Ask pupils to work in groups to carry out the activity. Explain that they need to regroup the tens, to tens and ones, so that they can share the tens equally. If necessary, show the following:

  7 tens → 6 tens + 1 ten
  5 tens → 3 tens + 2 tens
  9 tens → 8 tens + 1 ten

4

- Ask pupils to work through the exercises. If necessary, they can use base ten equipment to help them divide.

5 and **6**

- Pupils should work in pairs to solve the word problems. They should write a division statement based on each word problem.

Learning objectives: Division with regrouping in hundreds, tens and ones

Pupils will be able to:

- use concrete representations in a place value chart to show regrouping from hundreds to tens, then from tens to ones in division

- divide a 3-digit number by a 1-digit number with regrouping from hundreds to tens, then from tens to ones with or without remainder

- carry out the procedures in division starting from tens with regrouping and followed by ones

- solve simple word problems involving division of a 3-digit number by a 1-digit number with regrouping from hundreds to tens, then from tens to ones, with or without remainder

Key concepts

- Expressing a number as a sum of values of different places

- Dividing equally with or without remainder

- Regrouping from values of a higher place (e.g., hundreds) to a lower place (e.g., tens) in division

Teaching sequence

- Explain that when dividing 525 by 3, we have to write 525 as a sum of values of hundreds, tens and ones. Demonstrate this with a place value chart:
  525 = 5 hundreds 2 tens and 5 ones

- Show 5 hundreds 2 tens 5 ones using base ten equipment in a place value chart.

- Demonstrate, using concrete representations, that 5 hundreds has to be regrouped so that it can be divided evenly without a remainder.

Unit 7 Division

Let's Learn!

Division with regrouping in hundreds, tens and ones

Farmer Jones sells his crops to 3 restaurants. He divides 525 cabbages equally between the 3 restaurants. How many cabbages does each restaurant receive?

$525 \div 3 = ?$

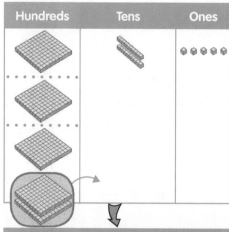

First divide the **hundreds** by 3.

5 hundreds $\div$ 3
= 1 hundred with remainder 2 hundreds

$$\begin{array}{r} 1 \\ 3\overline{)5\ 2\ 5} \\ \underline{3} \\ 2 \end{array}$$

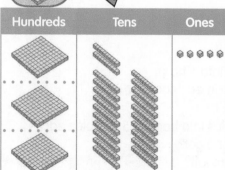

Regroup the remainder hundreds:
2 hundreds = 20 tens

Add the tens:
20 tens + 2 tens = 22 tens

$$\begin{array}{r} 1 \\ 3\overline{)5\ 2\ 5} \\ \underline{3} \\ 2\ 2 \end{array}$$

104

Thinking skills
- Associating
- Identifying relationships
- Recalling and relating multiplication and division facts

Heuristic for problem solving
Looking for patterns

Division **Unit 7**

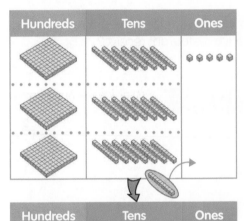

Hundreds	Tens	Ones

Then divide the **tens** by 3.

22 tens ÷ 3
= 7 tens with remainder 1 ten

```
    1 7
3) 5 2 5
   3
   2 2
   2 1
     1
```

Hundreds	Tens	Ones

Regroup the remainder ten:
1 ten = 10 ones

Add the ones:
10 ones + 5 ones = 15 ones

```
    1 7
3) 5 2 5
   3
   2 2
   2 1
   1 5
```

Hundreds	Tens	Ones

Finally divide the **ones** by 3.

15 ones ÷ 3 = 5 ones

```
    1 7 5
3) 5 2 5
   3
   2 2
   2 1
   1 5
   1 5
     0
```

So 525 ÷ 3 = 175.

Each restaurant receives 175 cabbages.

105

Teaching sequence

5 hundreds
= 3 hundreds + 2 hundreds
= 3 hundreds + 20 tens

5 hundreds 2 tens
= 3 hundreds + 20 tens
  + 2 tens
= 3 hundreds + 22 tens
= 3 hundreds + 21 tens + 1 ten
= 3 hundreds + 21 tens +
  10 ones

5 hundreds 2 tens 5 ones
= 3 hundreds + 21 tens +
  10 ones + 5 ones
= 3 hundreds + 21 tens +
  15 ones

- Demonstrate the division using a place value chart and base ten equipment as in the example in the textbook.

Additional activity

Show the following divisions with regrouping using concrete representations:

(1) $4\overline{)800}$ (2) $4\overline{)840}$

(3) $4\overline{)960}$ (4) $4\overline{)980}$

Teaching sequence

- Ask pupils to work in pairs for this exercise. Emphasise the importance of the place value of each digit and the steps involved in division.
- Divide the hundreds to obtain hundreds and a remainder. Regroup the remainder into hundreds and tens. Regroup 2 hundreds into tens. Add the tens to the existing tens and then divide. Regroup the tens into ones. Add the ones to the existing ones. Then divide the ones.

② Farmer Jones divides 735 carrots equally among 3 restaurants. How many carrots does each restaurant receive?

$735 \div 3 = ?$

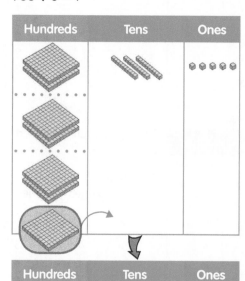

First divide the **hundreds** by 3.

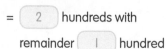

7 hundreds ÷ 3

= ⬚ 2 ⬚ hundreds with

remainder ⬚ 1 ⬚ hundred

Regroup the remainder hundred:

⬚ 1 ⬚ hundred = ⬚ 10 ⬚ tens

Add the tens:

⬚ 10 ⬚ tens + ⬚ 3 ⬚ tens

= ⬚ 13 ⬚ tens

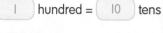

106

Additional activity

Ask pupils to work in pairs.
Ask them to find the missing numbers for the following:

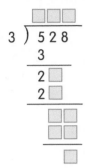

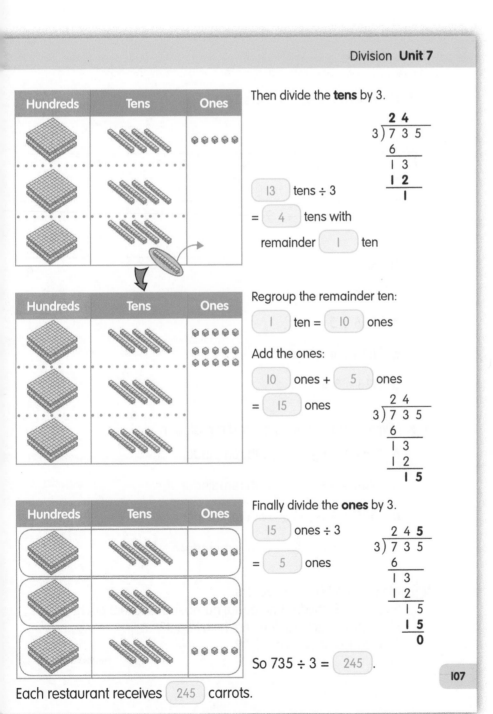

Hundreds	Tens	Ones

Then divide the **tens** by 3.

$$3\overline{)\,7\ 3\ 5}$$
$$\frac{6}{1\ 3}$$
$$\frac{1\ 2}{1}$$

13 tens ÷ 3

= 4 tens with

remainder 1 ten

Hundreds	Tens	Ones

Regroup the remainder ten:

1 ten = 10 ones

Add the ones:

10 ones + 5 ones

= 15 ones

$$3\overline{)\,7\ 3\ 5}$$
$$\frac{6}{1\ 3}$$
$$\frac{1\ 2}{1\ 5}$$

Hundreds	Tens	Ones

Finally divide the **ones** by 3.

15 ones ÷ 3

= 5 ones

$$3\overline{)\,7\ 3\ 5}$$
$$\frac{6}{1\ 3}$$
$$\frac{1\ 2}{1\ 5}$$
$$\frac{1\ 5}{0}$$

So 735 ÷ 3 = 245 .

Each restaurant receives 245 carrots.

107

Practice 5 in Practice Book 3B, pp 51 to 54.

Note

It may help to use boxes for division, especially to show pupils where the numbers belong.

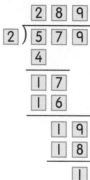

This is especially useful when a 3-digit number divides another number and gives an answer with 2 digits, or if there is a '0' in the answer.

E.g.

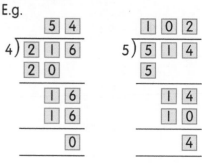

Teaching sequence

3 to **6**

* Pupils should work individually to answer these questions. Provide support to pupils as necessary.

Unit 7 Division

3 Find the missing numbers.

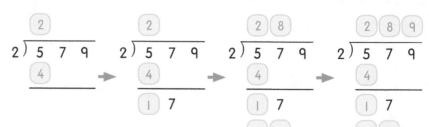

4 Divide.

a 338 ÷ 2 = 169

b 345 ÷ 5 = 69

c 656 ÷ 4 = 164

d 138 ÷ 3 = 46

5 Divide. Find the quotient and remainder.

a 357 ÷ 2 = 178 with remainder 1

b 269 ÷ 3 = 89 with remainder 2

c 525 ÷ 4 = 131 with remainder 1

d 468 ÷ 5 = 93 with remainder 3

6 Miss Smith has 263 stickers.
She gives 8 children an equal number of stickers each.
How many stickers does each child get? 32 stickers
How many stickers are left? 7 stickers

Practice Book 3B, p.51

108

Objectives of activity

Pupils will be able to:

- discover a pattern in a magic square
- explore whether or not adding, subtracting, multiplying or dividing a number will produce the same pattern

Let's Explore!

7

12	2	16
14	10	6
4	18	8

This is a magic square. The sum of the numbers horizontally (↔), vertically (↕) and diagonally (↘) is the same.

Adding horizontally:
12 + 2 + 16 = 30

14 + ⟨10⟩ + ⟨6⟩ = ⟨30⟩

4 + ⟨18⟩ + ⟨8⟩ = ⟨30⟩

Adding vertically:
12 + 14 + 4 = ⟨30⟩

2 + 10 + 18 = ⟨30⟩

16 + 6 + 8 = ⟨30⟩

Adding diagonally:
12 + 10 + 8 = ⟨30⟩

16 + ⟨10⟩ + ⟨4⟩ = ⟨30⟩

There is a pattern.
That's why this is called a magic square.

a Think of a number.
Add it to each number in the magic square.
Do you see a pattern? Is this a magic square? Yes

b Think of another number.
Subtract it from each number in the magic square.
Do you see a pattern? Is this a magic square? Yes

c Think of another number. Multiply or divide each number in the magic square by this number.
Do you see a pattern? Is this a magic square? Yes

109

Teaching sequence

7 *Let's Explore!*

- Pupils should find the sums of the numbers horizontally, vertically and diagonally.
- They should discover a pattern – sequential numbers placed at specific positions.
- Pupils can add/subtract/ multiply/divide each of the numbers in the magic square by the same number to make a magic square where the sum of numbers (horizontally, vertically and diagonally) are the same.

Objectives of activities

Pupils will be able to:

- use deduction to find unknown values to solve problems in long division
- reflect on the division procedures to check if the given methods are correct

Additional activity

Ask pupils to set division questions (with missing numbers) for their friends to answer.

Thinking skills

- Associating
- Identifying relationships
- Relating multiplication and division facts

Independent work

Maths Journal, Challenging Practice and *Problem Solving* in Practice Book 3B, pp 55 to 58.

Teaching sequence

8 *Put On Your Thinking Caps!*

- Ask pupils to find the missing numbers in the number puzzles.
- Guide pupils to see that:
  3 tens × 5 = 15 tens
  17 tens is 2 tens more than 15 tens.
  So the missing digit is 7.

9 *Maths Journal*

- Pupils should spot the mistakes in the notes. The correct answers are:

  (a) When an odd number is divided by 2, there is always a remainder of 1.

  (b) When an even number is divided by 2, there is no remainder.

  (c) Divide the tens first then the ones.

  (d) When we divide a number by another, the result is called a quotient, any number left is called a remainder

  Note: Review the concept of division as necessary with the class.

Unit 7 Division

Put On Your Thinking Caps!

8 Find the missing numbers.

```
      4 5
  2 ) 9 (0)
      8
    ─────
    1 0
    1 0
    ─────
      0
```

```
      3 4
  5 ) 1 (7) 1
      1 5
    ─────
      2 1
      2 0
    ─────
        1
```

> Practice Book 3B, p.57   Practice Book 3B, p.58

Maths Journal

9 Find the mistakes in these statements.

  a When an odd number is divided by 2, there is no remainder.
  a   When an odd number is divided by 2, there is a remainder.
  b When an even number is divided by 2, there is a remainder.
  b   When an even number is divided by 2, there is no remainder.
  c We always begin to divide the ones first, then the tens for the following:

  3) 3 2   4) 2 6   5) 7 1

  d When we divide one number by another, the result is called a remainder.
    Any number left is called a quotient.
    d   When we divide one number by another, the result is called a quotient. Any number left is called a remainder.

  Explain the mistakes.

  c   We always begin to divide the tens first, then the ones for the following:

```
      1 0          6           1 4
  3 ) 3 2     4 ) 2 6     5 ) 7 1
      3           2 4           5
    ─────       ─────         ─────
      2           2             2 1
                                2 0
                              ─────
                                  1
```

110

Unit 7 Division

Date: _____

Practice I Quotient and remainder

1 Answer these questions.

a 31 ones ÷ 4 = [7] r [3]

Quotient   = [7] ones

Remainder = [3] ones

b 24 ones ÷ 3 = [8] r [0]

Quotient   = [8] ones

Remainder = [0] ones

2 Find the quotient.

Example

```
     [9]
3 ) 2  7
    [2][7]
       [0]
```

a

```
      [4]
4 ) 1  6
   [1][6]
      [0]
```

b

```
     [6]
4 ) 2  4
   [2][4]
      [0]
```

c

```
      [9]
5 ) 4  5
   [4][5]
      [0]
```

43

Unit 7: Division

Answers Unit 7: Division   193

Practice 2 Odd and even numbers

1 Circle the correct word.

a Is 21 an even number? [Yes] (**No**)

How do you know? When 21 is divided by 2, it has (**a**) [no] remainder.

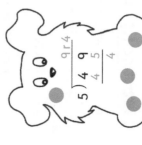

b Is 32 an odd number? [Yes] (**No**)

How do you know? When 32 is divided by 2, it has [a] (**no**) remainder.

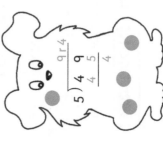

2 Divide each of these numbers by 2. Is each number odd or even?
Then answer questions **a** and **b**.

```
    7              1 1
2 ) 1 4        2 ) 2 3
    1 4            2 2
      0              1

    1 4            1 4
2 ) 2 9        2 ) 2 8
    2 8            2 8
      1              0
```

a __14__ is an even number.
It does not have a __remainder__ when divided by __2__.

b __23__ and __29__ are odd numbers.
They have a __remainder__ of __1__ when divided
by __2__.

---

3 Divide.
The remainder tells you how many spots each dog has.
Draw the correct number of spots on each dog.

Example

```
    7 r 2
3 ) 2 3
    2 1
      2
```

Quotient = **7** ones
Remainder = **2** ones

a

```
    8 r 3
4 ) 3 5
    3 2
      3
```

Quotient = **8** ones
Remainder = **3** ones

b

```
    7 r 1
5 ) 3 6
    3 5
      1
```

Quotient = **7** ones
Remainder = **1** one

c

```
    9 r 4
5 ) 4 9
    4 5
      4
```

Quotient = **9** ones
Remainder = **4** ones

3 Look at the numbers below.

76 11 30 68 84
92 59 95 123 477 980

a Circle all the **even numbers** and write them down.

30, 68, 76, 84, 92, 980

b Write down all the **odd numbers**.

11, 59, 95, 123, 477

c Write down:

the ones digit in the even numbers in **a.**

0, 2, 4, 6, 8

the ones digit in the odd numbers in **b.**

1, 3, 5, 7, 9

4 Fill in the spaces.

a Use the digits 4, 5, 2 and 9 to make the greatest 4-digit **odd number**.

9425

b Use the digits 0, 1, 6 and 9 to make the smallest 4-digit **even number**. (Do not begin with zero.)

1096

Practice 3 Division without remainder and regrouping

1 Divide.
Match the answers to the correct place value charts.

a 12 ones ÷ 2 = __6__ ones

b 21 ones ÷ 3 = __7__ ones

c 44 ones ÷ 4 = __1__ ten __1__ one

d 69 ones ÷ 3 = __2__ tens __3__ ones

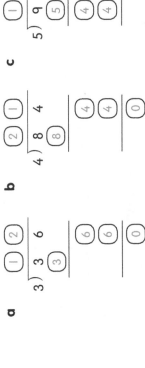

2 Answer these questions.

a
```
    1 2
3 ) 3 6
    3
    6
    6
    0
```

b
```
    2 1
4 ) 8 4
    8
    4
    4
    0
```

c
```
    1 9
5 ) 9 5
    5
    4 5
    4 5
    0
```

3 Match the squirrels to the correct trees.

Trees: 42 ÷ 2   44 ÷ 4   96 ÷ 3   82 ÷ 2   46 ÷ 2   75 ÷ 5

Squirrels: 11   32   21   15   41   23

Date: _____

Practice 4 Division with regrouping in tens and ones

1 Divide.

C
```
    1 6
2 ) 3 2
    2
  - 2 2
  - 2
      0
```

M
```
    2 6
3 ) 7 8
    6
  - 1 8
  - 1 8
      0
```

R
```
    2 7 r2
3 ) 8 3
    6
  - 2 3
  - 2 1
      2
```

I
```
    2 3
4 ) 9 2
    8
  - 1 2
  - 1 2
      0
```

F
```
    1 7 r1
4 ) 6 9
    4
  - 2 9
  - 2 8
      1
```

A
```
    1 5
5 ) 7 5
    5
  - 2 5
  - 2 5
      0
```

T
```
    1 2 r3
5 ) 6 3
    5
  - 1 3
  - 1 0
      3
```

J
```
    3 6
2 ) 7 2
    6
  - 1 2
  - 1 2
      0
```

What kind of jam can't be eaten?
Match the letters to the quotients below.

T	R	A	F	F	I	C		J	A	M
12	27	15	17	17	23	16		36	15	26

2

Farmer Mary picks apples from her orchard.
She puts her apples into four buckets.
She can only sell apples from the buckets that have quotients without remainders.
Which buckets can she sell from?

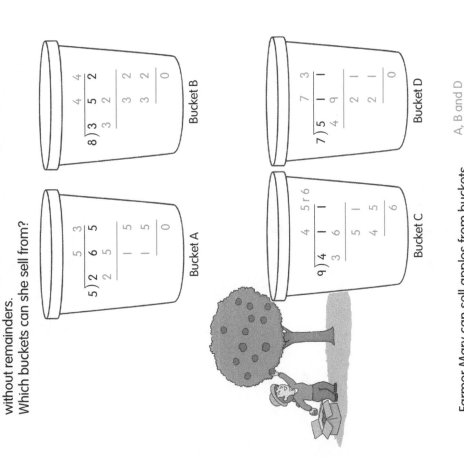

Bucket A
$$5)\overline{265} = 53$$

Bucket B
$$8)\overline{352} = 44$$

Bucket C
$$9)\overline{414} = 45\ r\ 6$$

Bucket D
$$7)\overline{511} = 73$$

Farmer Mary can sell apples from buckets __A, B and D__.

Date: _____

Practice 5   Division with regrouping in hundreds, tens and ones

1 Ella can't remember the steps for division.
Help her to complete the steps.

a $3)\overline{468} = 156$

b $4)\overline{936} = 234$

Page 52

2 Divide and complete the number puzzle.

Down

a
```
    3 9 9
2)7 9 8
  6
  -1 9
   1 8
   -1 8
      0
```

b
```
    2 8 3
3)8 4 9
  6
  2 4
  2 4
    9
    9
    0
```

c
```
    1 7 4
4)6 9 6
  4
  2 9
  2 8
    1 6
    1 6
      0
```

Across

d
```
    1 3 9
5)6 9 5
  5
  1 9
  1 5
    4 5
    4 5
      0
```

e
```
    3 7 7
2)7 5 4
  6
  1 5
  1 4
    1 4
    1 4
      0
```

f
```
    9 3
4)3 7 2
  3 6
    1 2
    1 2
      0
```

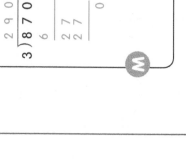

Page 53

3 Divide.

S
```
    1 7 3
2)3 4 6
  2
  1 4
  1 4
    6
    6
    0
```

T
```
    1 9 0 r1
4)7 6 1
  4
  3 6
  3 6
    1
```

U
```
    1 6 3
3)4 8 9
  3
  1 8
  1 8
    9
    9
    0
```

E
```
    1 7 1 r4
5)8 5 9
  5
  3 5
  3 5
    9
    5
    4
```

M
```
    2 9 0
3)8 7 0
  6
  2 7
  2 7
    0
```

P
```
    1 3 2
4)5 2 8
  4
  1 2
  1 2
    8
    8
    0
```

K
```
    1 4 1
5)7 0 5
  5
  2 0
  2 0
    5 5
    5 5
     0
```

R
```
    1 2 5 r2
3)3 7 7
  3
    7
    6
    1 7
    1 5
      2
```

Which pet makes the loudest noise?
Match the letters to the quotients below.

T	R	U	M	P	E	T
190	125	163	290	132	171	190

4 Divide.

a $516 \div 2 =$ __258__

b $145 \div 3 =$ __48 r 1__

c $399 \div 4 =$ __99 r 3__

d $885 \div 5 =$ __177__

5 Divide.
Match the answers.

a $80 \div 4$

b $191 \div 3$

c $407 \div 4$

d $75 \div 5$

e $121 \div 3$

S 20
D 63 r 2
I 101 r 3
A 15
E 40 r 1

Find Millie's favourite flowers.
Match the letters to the quotients below.

D	A	I	S	I	E	S
63	15	101	20	101	40	20

Date: _____

Maths Journal

1 Look at these steps for division.

Step 1	Step 2	Step 3	Step 4	Step 5
1 5)6 9 5 5 1	1 5)6 9 5 5 1 9	1 3 5)6 9 5 5 1 9 1 5 4	1 3 5)6 9 5 5 1 9 1 5 4 5	1 3 9 5)6 9 5 5 1 9 1 5 4 5 4 5 0

Help Jack to write the steps for division in order.
Write the step numbers in the [blob].

Divide the hundreds by 5. Step 1

Divide the ones by 5. Step 5

Divide the tens by 5. Step 3

Regroup the remainder hundreds and then add the tens. Step 2

Regroup the remainder tens and then add the ones. Step 4

Page 56

2 Complete the following division.

Step 1	Step 2	Step 3	Step 4	Step 5

1
4)7 5 2
  4
	1
	4)7 5 2
	  4 0
	  3 5
		1 8
		4)7 5 2
		  4 0
		  3 5
		  3 2
		    3
			1 8
			4)7 5 2
			  4 0
			  3 5
			  3 2
			    3 2
				1 8 8
				4)7 5 2
				  4 0
				  3 5
				  3 2
				    3 2
				       0

Write the steps, using Question 1 as a guide.

Step 1: Divide the hundreds by 4.

Step 2: Regroup the remainder hundreds and then add the tens.

Step 3: Divide the tens by 4.

Step 4: Regroup the remainder tens and then add the ones.

Step 5: Divide the ones by 4.

Page 57

Date: _____

Challenging Practice

1 Find the sum of all the odd numbers between 60 and 66.

```
   6 1
   6 3
 + 6 5
 ─────
 1 8 9
```

2 Colour the correct division sentences.

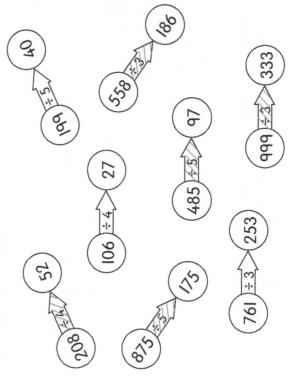

- 199 ÷ 5 → 40
- 558 ÷ 3 → 186
- 52 → ÷ 4 → 208
- 106 ÷ 4 → 27
- 485 ÷ 5 → 97
- 875 ÷ 5 → 175
- 999 ÷ 3 → 333
- 761 ÷ 3 → 253

Date: _____

1 Mrs Williams buys a tin of biscuits.
The number of biscuits is fewer than 60 but more than 40.
She would have 2 biscuits left if she divided the biscuits equally between 10 children.
She would also have 2 biscuits left if she divided them equally between 8 children.
How many biscuits are in the tin?

Use the chart below to help you solve the word problem.

Number of biscuits	Divide between 10 children	Divide between 8 children	Check
59	5 r 9	7 r 3	✗
52	5 r 2	6 r 4	✗
48	4 r 8	6	✗
42	4 r 2	5 r 2	✓

There are ___42___ biscuits in the tin.

Unit 8: Solving Word Problems 2: Multiplication and Division

Week	Learning Objectives	Thinking Skills	Resources
5	**(1) Multiplication: one-step word problems** Pupils will be able to: • solve one-step word problems on multiplication using model drawing • interpret the terms 'how many times as many as' and 'how many times another number' and draw a model to represent a problem situation • use the 'group and item' concept and model to solve word problems	• Recalling and applying multiplication facts Heuristic for problem solving: • Drawing a model to represent a problem situation	• Pupil Textbook 3A, pp 111 to 112 • Practice Book 3B, pp 59 to 60 • Teacher's Guide 3A, pp 205 to 206
5–6	**(2) Multiplication: two-step word problems** Pupils will be able to: • solve two-step word problems on multiplication using model drawing • interpret and apply multiplication, addition and subtraction concepts to model drawing and problem solving • write two-step word problems: (a) using given words and numbers (b) by interpreting a given model	• Recalling and applying multiplication facts • Applying addition and subtraction concepts to problem solving	• Pupil Textbook 3A, pp 113 to 116 • Practice Book 3B, pp 61 to 66 • Teacher's Guide 3A, pp 207 to 210

Unit 8: Solving Word Problems 2: Multiplication and Division

Medium-term plan

Week	Learning Objectives	Thinking Skills	Resources
6	**(3) Division: one-step word problems** Pupils will be able to: • solve one-step word problems on division using model drawing • interpret and apply division concepts to model drawing to represent a problem situation • use the unitary method to solve division problems	• Recalling and applying division concepts Heuristic for problem solving: • Drawing a model to represent a problem situation	• Pupil Textbook 3A, pp 117 to 119 • Practice Book 3B, pp 67 to 70 • Teacher's Guide 3A, pp 211 to 213

6	**(4) Division: two-step word problems**
	
	Pupils will be able to:
	• solve two-step word problems using other operational concepts with division concepts
	• draw models to represent the two steps in solving the word problems
	• write two-step word problems:
	  (a) using given words and numbers
	  (b) by interpreting a given model
		• Recalling and applying division concepts with multiplication
		• Applying addition and subtraction concepts to problem solving
			• Pupil Textbook 3A, pp 120 to 123
			• Practice Book 3B, pp 71 to 75
			• Teacher's Guide 3A, pp 214 to 217

Unit 8: Solving Word Problems 2: Multiplication and Division

Medium-term plan

Week	Learning Objectives	Thinking Skills	Resources
6	*Put On Your Thinking Caps!* Pupils will be able to: • use model drawing to solve challenging word problems • draw a diagram or apply 'guess and check' to solve challenging word problems	Heuristic for problem solving: • Guess and check	• Pupil Textbook 3A, p 123 • Practice Book 3B, pp 76 to 78 • Teacher's Guide 3A, p 217

Solving Word Problems 2: Multiplication and Division

Learning objectives:
Multiplication: one-step word problems

Pupils will be able to:

- solve one-step word problems on multiplication using model drawing

- interpret the terms 'how many times as many as' and 'how many times another number' and draw a model to represent a problem situation

- use the 'group and item' concept and model to solve word problems

Key concepts

- The multiple concept in multiplication is used to compare two sets of items.
- Bar diagrams can be based on problem situations in multiplication.

Unit 8 — Solving Word Problems 2: Multiplication and Division

Let's Learn!

Multiplication: one-step word problems

1 Hardeep has 542 stamps. Jack has twice as many stamps as Hardeep. How many stamps does Jack have?

542 stamps

Hardeep

Jack

?

> Twice is 2 times.
> ☐ stands for 542 stamps.
> So ☐☐ stands for 542 stamps × 2.

542 × 2 = 1084

Jack has 1084 stamps.

2 Sarah sells 750 flowers. Ben sells 3 times the number of flowers Sarah sells. How many flowers does Ben sell?

750 flowers

Sarah

Ben

> ☐ stands for 750 flower.
> So ☐☐☐ stands for 750 flowers × 3.

⟨ 2250 ⟩ flowers

⟨ 750 ⟩ × ⟨ 3 ⟩ = ⟨ 2250 ⟩

Ben sells ⟨ 2250 ⟩ flowers.

III

Teaching sequence

1

- Explain the meaning of the term 'twice as many as'.
- It indicates the number of items Hardeep has versus the number of items Jack has. Represent the problem situation using models. In the example, we represent the number of items Hardeep has by 1 bar, and the number of items Jack has by 2 bars.
- **Note**: The bar indicates the number of items and not the person.

2

- Explain that '3 times the number of' has the same meaning as '3 times as many as'.
- Ask pupils to fill in the missing numbers on the model to assess whether they can interpret the problem situation and use model drawing to solve it.
- Note that pupils should have the following basic skills before they can work on this Unit:
  1) Multiply a 3-digit number by a 1-digit number.
  2) Draw bars of the same length to represent the same quantity.

Thinking skill

Recalling and applying multiplication facts

Heuristic for problem solving

Drawing a model to represent a problem situation

Additional activity

Ask pupils to work in pairs. Pupil A writes statements like this:

I unit → 7 apples

5 units → 5 × 7 = 35 apples

Pupil B draws a model representing the information and fills in as much information as possible.

Independent work

Practice I in Practice Book 3B, pp 59 to 60.

Teaching sequence

 3

- Explain to pupils that the problem is similar to **1** and **2** but a different method (the unitary method) is used to find the answer.
- Explain that I part of the model is represented as I unit. The number of parts can be found by relating the value of each part or unit.

 4

- Ask pupils to read the problem and relate it to the model. Pupils should solve the problem and fill in the unknown values by interpreting the model.

Unit 8 Solving Word Problems 2: Multiplication and Division

3 Millie buys 5 packets of football stickers.
Each packet contains I2 football stickers.
How many football stickers does she buy altogether?

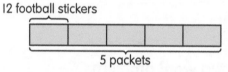

I unit → I2

5 units → I2 × 5 = 60

She buys 60 football stickers altogether.

4 Rosa saves £I95 each month.
Mario saves 3 times as much money as Rosa each month.
How much money does Mario save in a month?

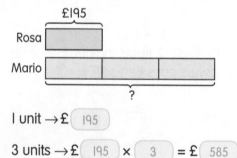

I unit → £ (I95)

3 units → £ (I95) × (3) = £ (585)

Mario saves £ (585) in a month.

Practice Book 3B, p.59

II2

Pupils will be able to:

- solve two-step word problems on multiplication using model drawing
- interpret and apply multiplication, addition and subtraction concepts to model drawing and problem solving
- write two-step word problems:
  (a) using given words and numbers
  (b) by interpreting a given model

Key concepts

- Multiplication concepts including 'multiple' and 'group and item' are used for solving two-step word problems.
- Addition concepts such as 'adding on' and 'part-whole' are used for solving two-step word problems.
- Subtraction concepts such as 'taking away' and 'part-whole' are used for solving two-step word problems.

Thinking skills

- Recalling and applying multiplication facts
- Applying addition and subtraction concepts to problem solving

---

Solving Word Problems 2: Multiplication and Division   **Unit 8**

Let's Learn!

Multiplication: two-step word problems

1 A service station sold 273 litres of petrol. A supermarket sold double the amount of petrol.
  a How many litres of petrol did the supermarket sell?
  b How many litres of petrol did they sell altogether?

Double means 2 times.

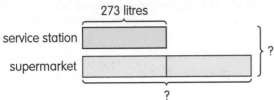

273 litres

service station

supermarket

?

?

a $273 \times 2 = 546$

The supermarket sold 546 litres of petrol.

b $273 + 546 = 819$

They sold 819 litres of petrol altogether.

113

Teaching sequence

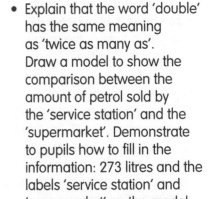

- Revise the 'multiple' concept in multiplication and 'part-whole' concept in addition. These two concepts are prerequisites to solving this question.

- Explain that the word 'double' has the same meaning as 'twice as many as'. Draw a model to show the comparison between the amount of petrol sold by the 'service station' and the 'supermarket'. Demonstrate to pupils how to fill in the information: 273 litres and the labels 'service station' and 'supermarket' on the model.

- Explain that the first part requires the use of the 'multiple' concept to find the amount of petrol sold by the supermarket. The second part requires the use of the 'part-whole' concept to find the total amount of petrol sold by the service station and the supermarket. Fill in the question marks on the model to show the unknown values to be found. Show the steps needed to solve the problem.

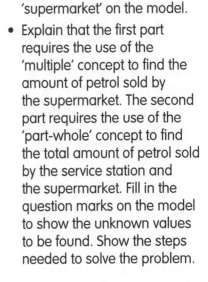

Additional activity

Ask pupils to write a word problem based on this model.

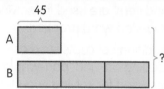

Teaching sequence

2

- Revise the 'group and item' concept in multiplication and the 'taking away' concept in subtraction. These two concepts are prerequisites to solving this question.
- Explain the 'group and item' concept using this question: 8 bags refer to 8 groups of items and the number 156 refers to the number of items in the bags. Demonstrate how the model is drawn. Talk about the model and write the multiplication sentence to find the number of peanuts Mrs Cheng had to begin with. Ask pupils to fill in the missing values in the multiplication sentence.
- Explain the 'taking away' concept: Mrs Cheng had some peanuts and gave 382 of them to her children. Demonstrate how the model is drawn. Talk about the model and write the subtraction sentence. Ask pupils to complete the subtraction sentence.

3

- Explain to pupils that this question is similar to the previous questions. It involves two steps. The 'part-whole' and 'group and item' concepts are prerequisites to solving the problem.
- Highlight that the unitary method is also another way to solve the problem.
- Ask pupils to read the problem and fill in the unknown values to solve the problem.

Unit 8 Solving Word Problems 2: Multiplication and Division

2 Mrs Cheng has 8 bags of peanuts. Each bag contains 156 peanuts. She gives 382 peanuts to her children. How many peanuts are left?

Find the number of peanuts Mrs Cheng had to begin with.

$\boxed{156} \times \boxed{8} = \boxed{1248}$

Mrs Cheng had $\boxed{1248}$ peanuts to begin with.

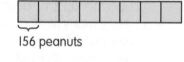

156 peanuts

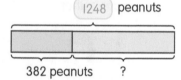

$\boxed{1248}$ peanuts

$\boxed{1248} - \boxed{382} = \boxed{866}$

$\boxed{866}$ peanuts are left.

382 peanuts   ?

3 Jack has some apples and oranges. He puts 3 oranges and 4 apples into each box. He has a total of 5 boxes of fruit. How many pieces of fruit are there altogether?

$\boxed{3} + \boxed{4} = \boxed{7}$

There are $\boxed{7}$ pieces of fruit in each box.

3 oranges   4 apples

I box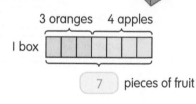

$\boxed{7}$ pieces of fruit

I box → $\boxed{7}$

5 boxes → $\boxed{7} \times 5 = \boxed{35}$

There are $\boxed{35}$ pieces of fruit altogether.

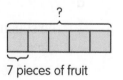

7 pieces of fruit

114

Additional activity

Ask pupils to write a two-step word problem based on this model.

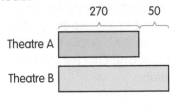

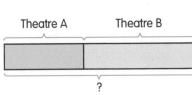

Solving Word Problems 2: Multiplication and Division **Unit 8**

4 Tai saves 4 times as much money as Farha.
Ruby saves £12 less than Tai.
Farha saves £32.
How much money does Ruby save?

I unit → £ 32

4 units → £ 32 × 4 = £ 128

Tai saves £ 128 .

£ 128 – £ 12 = £ 116

Ruby saves £ 116 .

5 For each of these word problems, think whether you should add, subtract or multiply at each step.
Then solve the problem.

a The cost of one cinema ticket is £5.
Miya buys 8 tickets and has £25 left.
How much money did she have to begin with? £65

b Ella makes a necklace with 12 red beads and 15 yellow beads.
She makes a total of 9 necklaces.
How many beads does she use altogether? 243 beads

c Peter wants to make 8 cakes.
He uses 270 g of flour and 41 g of sugar to make one cake.
How much flour and sugar does he use altogether? 2488 g

115

Teaching sequence

4

- Ask pupils to read the problem. If necessary, explain that the comparing concept is used in the problems. Ask them to fill in the unknown values from the given model and solve the problem.

5

- Ask pupils to read the problems and draw appropriate models to solve them.

Teaching sequence

a

- Guide pupils to select the key statements to help write sentences for the problem. If necessary, explain how to make a sentence.
  - Subject (a person)
  - Mathematical statement (twice as many as)
  - Object (pencils)
  - Subject (a person)
  - Ella has twice as many pencils as Farha.
- Ask pupils to work in pairs to write and solve a two-step word problem using the helping words and numbers.
- Guide pupils to:
  1) look at the words and think of two parts of a word problem
  2) recall the concepts of multiplication and apply them to the first part of the word problem
  3) think of an addition or subtraction concept and apply it to the second part of the word problem
- The following is a sample two-step word problem:
  Ella had twice as many pencils as Farha.
  Farha had 745 pencils.
  i. How many pencils did Ella have?
  ii. How many pencils did they have altogether?

b

- Help pupils to relate the model to the four operation concepts. You can make a list of the concepts to help them choose the correct one.

Independent work

Practice 2 in Practice Book 3B, pp 61 to 66.

Additional activity

Ask pupils to work in pairs. Pupil A writes a one-step word problem. Pupil B then adds some words or sentences to change it into a two-step word problem. Both pupils solve the problem and check each other's answers.

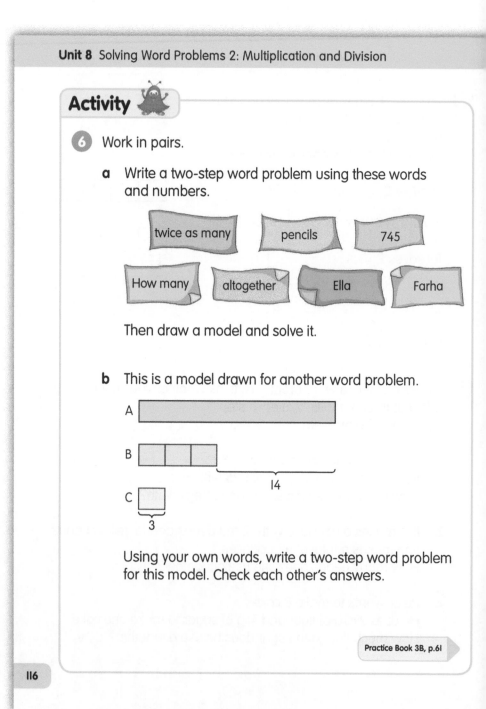

Unit 8 Solving Word Problems 2: Multiplication and Division

Activity

6 Work in pairs.

a Write a two-step word problem using these words and numbers.

> twice as many   pencils   745
>
> How many   altogether   Ella   Farha

Then draw a model and solve it.

b This is a model drawn for another word problem.

A

B ___ 14

C 3

Using your own words, write a two-step word problem for this model. Check each other's answers.

Practice Book 3B, p.61

116

Learning objectives:
Division: one-step word problems

Pupils will be able to:

- solve one-step word problems on division using model drawing
- interpret and apply division concepts to model drawing to represent a problem situation
- use the unitary method to solve division problems

Key concepts

- The division concepts: finding the number of groups and the number of items in each group are applied.
- Division is the inverse of multiplication.

Thinking skill

Recalling and applying division concepts

Heuristic for problem solving

Drawing a model to represent a problem situation

Let's Learn!

Division: one-step word problems

1 A farmer picks 875 apples from her orchard.
She packs them equally into 5 boxes.
How many apples does she pack in each box?

875 apples

?

$875 \div 5 = 175$

She packs 175 apples in each box.

2 Hardeep's dad buys 486 fish and puts them into fish tanks.
Each fish tank holds 9 fish.
How many fish tanks does Hardeep's dad use?

486 fish

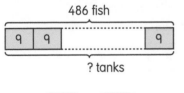

? tanks

$486 \div \boxed{9} = \boxed{54}$

Hardeep's dad uses 54 fish tanks.

II7

Teaching sequence

1

- Revise the concept of division as the inverse of multiplication. In multiplication, the total number of items is found by multiplying the number of items in each group by the number of groups. In division, the number of items in each group is found by dividing the total number of items by the number of groups.

- This example illustrates the concept of division by finding the number of apples in each box (number of items in each group) given the total number of apples. Explain to pupils how the model is drawn to represent the problem situation.

2

- This example illustrates the concept of division by finding the number of fish tanks (number of groups) given the total number of fish. Explain to pupils how the model is drawn to represent the problem situation.

- Point out to pupils the differences between the models in examples **1** and **2**.

Additional activity

Ask pupils to work in pairs. Ask each pair to write a one-step word problem based on each model.

(1)

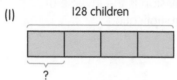

128 children

?

(2)

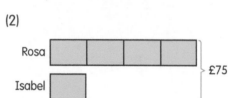

Rosa

Isabel

£75

Teaching sequence

- Ask pupils to read, interpret and solve the problem.

- Explain to pupils that this problem is similar to the previous problems. However, it involves a different method to find the answer.

- Highlight the unitary method to solve the problem.

- Help pupils to read the problem and relate it to the model. Explain the steps in the unitary method to find the answer.

- Ask pupils to read the problem. Ask them to interpret the model and fill in the unknown information to solve the problem.

③ The baker makes 128 scones.
He packs them equally into 4 boxes.
How many scones does he pack into each box?

$\boxed{128}$ ÷ $\boxed{4}$ = $\boxed{32}$

He packs $\boxed{32}$ scones into each box.

$\boxed{128}$ scones

$\boxed{32}$ scones

④ Rosa's grandpa gives £36 to Rosa and her sister.
Rosa receives 3 times as much money as her sister.
How much money does her sister receive?

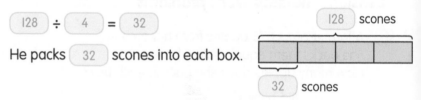

4 units → £36
I unit → £36 ÷ 4 = £9

Rosa

Rosa's sister

£36

Rosa's sister receives £9.

⑤ A supermarket sells 32 bananas.
It sells 4 times as many bananas as a greengrocer.
How many bananas does the greengrocer sell?

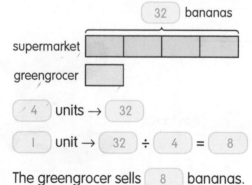

$\boxed{32}$ bananas

supermarket

greengrocer

$\boxed{4}$ units → $\boxed{32}$

$\boxed{I}$ unit → $\boxed{32}$ ÷ $\boxed{4}$ = $\boxed{8}$

The greengrocer sells $\boxed{8}$ bananas.

118

Independent work

Practices 3 and 4 in Practice
Book 3B, pp 67 to 70.

Solving Word Problems 2: Multiplication and Division   **Unit 8**

6 Solve these word problems.

a Mr Lee packs 180 kg of rice into 5 kg bags.
How many bags does he use? 36 bags

b At the school fair, Peter sells 318 cups of lemonade.
He sells 3 times as many cups of lemonade as Omar.
How many cups of lemonade does Omar sell? 106 cups

c The total age of Emma and Hannah is 72 years.
Emma is thrice as old as Hannah.
How old is Hannah? 18 years old

Thrice means
3 times.

Activity

7 Write and solve division word problems using the words
and numbers in **a** and **b** .

a

Jack	orange juice
856 litres	4
equally	each container
containers	How many

b

Mr Taylor	pineapples
Each box	some boxes
728	9
packs	equally
How many	boxes

c This is a model drawn for a word problem.

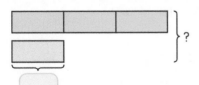

Using your own words, write a
division word problem for it.

Practice Book 3B, p.67 and 69

Teaching sequence

6

- Ask pupils to draw a model
  to solve each one-step word
  problem.

7

- Ask pupils to work in pairs
  to write and solve division
  problems using the helping
  words and numbers.

- Guide pupils to:
  1) read the words and
     relate them to the division
     concepts learnt earlier
  2) work out which question is
     to be asked: do we find
     the number of groups or
     the number of items in
     each group?
  3) write down part of the
     division problem using the
     given words. Then they
     should complete the
     problem in their own words.

- **Note**: Pupils could use
  additional words other than
  the ones given. The following
  are examples of one-step
  word problems:

- Jack had 856 litres of orange
  juice. He poured the orange
  juice equally into 4 containers.
  How much orange juice was
  there in each container?

- Mr Taylor had 728 pineapples.
  He packed them equally into
  some boxes so that each box
  contained 9 pineapples. How
  many boxes did Mr Taylor use?

Unit 8: Solving Word Problems 2: Multiplication and Division   **213**

Learning objectives: Division: two-step word problems

Pupils will be able to:

- solve two-step word problems using other operational concepts with division concepts

- draw models to represent the two steps in solving the word problems

- write two-step word problems:
  (a) using given words and numbers
  (b) by interpreting a given model

Teaching sequence

- Revise division concepts such as finding the number of items in each group. Also revise subtraction concepts such as 'taking away'. These are prerequisites for solving this problem.

- Explain and relate the 'taking away' concept to the given problem. Draw a model to illustrate the first step of the problem and on the model identify both the given and the unknown values. In the second step of the problem explain and relate the division concept of finding the number of items in each group. Draw a model to show this and make links with the model drawn in the first step.

- **Note**: Highlight the key words that reflect the concepts for model drawing. The two key words:

  Uses → to reflect the 'taking away' concept

  Equal bags → to reflect division

Key concepts

- Division concepts using 'group and item' are used for solving two-step word problems.

- Addition concepts such as 'adding on' and 'part-whole' are used for solving two-step word problems.

- Subtraction concepts such as 'taking away' and 'part-whole' are used for solving two-step word problems.

Thinking skills

- Recalling and applying division concepts with multiplication

- Applying addition and subtraction concepts to problem solving

---

Unit 8 Solving Word Problems 2: Multiplication and Division

Let's Learn!

| Division: two-step word problems |

1 Sam the baker has 795 g of flour.
He uses 145 g of it to make biscuits.
He puts the remaining flour into 5 equal bags.

   a How much flour is left?

   b What is the mass of each bag of flour?

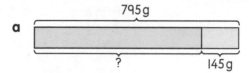

$795 - 145 = 650$

There is 650 g of flour left.

b

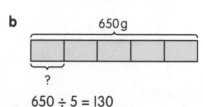

$650 \div 5 = 130$

The mass of each bag of flour is 130 g.

120

Additional activity

Ask pupils to work in pairs. Ask each pair to write a two-step word problem based on the following models.

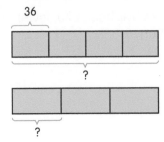

Solving Word Problems 2: Multiplication and Division   **Unit 8**

2 Ruby buys 3 bags of jelly beans.
Each bag contains 40 jelly beans.
She shares the jelly beans equally among 6 friends.
How many jelly beans does each friend get?

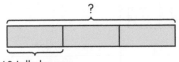

40 jelly beans

$40 \times 3 = 120$
Ruby buys 120 jelly beans.

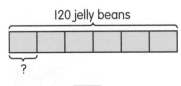

First find out how many jelly beans Ruby buys.

$120 \div 6 =$ [20]

Each friend gets [20] jelly beans.

3 Mr Jones buys 6 boxes of oranges.
Each box contains 36 oranges.
He packs the oranges into bags of 8 oranges each.
How many bags of oranges does he fill?

[36] × [6] = [216]

Mr Jones has [216] oranges.

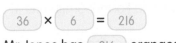

[216] ÷ [8] = [27]

He fills [27] bags of oranges.

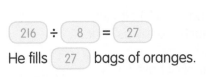

[216] oranges

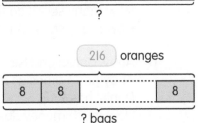

121

Teaching sequence

2

- Revise multiplication and division concepts such as 'group and item'.
- Explain and relate the multiplication concept to the given problem.
- The key words are '3 bags and 40 jelly beans in each bag'. Draw the model to show the known and unknown values. The unknown value is the total number of jelly beans Ruby buys.
- Explain and relate the division concept (finding the number of items in each group) to the given problem.
- The key words are 'shared between 6 friends'. Draw the second model to relate the information from the first model and the number of friends.

3

- Ask pupils to read and interpret the problem and link key words to the model. Pupils should solve the problems by interpreting the models. If necessary, highlight the key words:
  6 boxes and each contained 36 oranges → indicates multiplication 'group and item'.
  Packs them into bags of 8 → indicates division to find number of groups.

Practice 5 in Practice Book 3B,
pp 71 to 75.

Ask pupils to draw a model for
each set of words:

(1) Peter, Millie, three times as
many as

(2) Nick, Michael, £70, fewer
than

Teaching sequence

- Ask pupils to read and interpret
the problem and link key words
to the model. Pupils should
then solve the problem by
interpreting the model.

- If necessary, highlight the key
words:
'twice as many as' → indicates
multiple
concept.

- Ask pupils to read, interpret
and draw a model to solve
each problem. Highlight that
they need to identify some
key words to help them draw
suitable models. They should
preferably work in pairs for
discussion purposes.

Unit 8 Solving Word Problems 2: Multiplication and Division

4 Ella, Hardeep and Miya have 220 stickers altogether.
Ella has twice as many stickers as Hardeep.
Miya has 40 stickers.
How many stickers does Hardeep have?

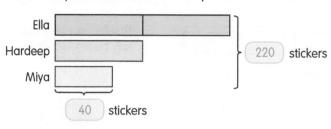

$$220 - 40 = 180$$

Ella and Hardeep have 180 stickers.

3 units → 180
1 unit → 180 ÷ 3 = 60
Hardeep has 60 stickers.

5 For each of these word problems, think whether you should add,
subtract, multiply or divide at each step. Then solve the problem.

a Farmer Jones has 328 seeds and Farmer Smith has 476 seeds.
They share the seeds equally.
How many seeds do they have altogether? 804 seeds
How many seeds are there in each equal share? 402 seeds

b Abby, Daniel and Nick have £360 altogether.
Abby has 4 times as much money as Nick.
Daniel has £45.
How much money does Nick have? £63

Practice Book 3B, p.71

122

Objectives of activity

Pupils will be able to:

- use model drawing to solve challenging word problems
- draw a diagram or apply 'guess and check' to solve challenging word problems

Heuristic for problem solving

Guess and check

Independent work

Maths Journal, Challenging Practice and *Problem Solving* in Practice Book 3B, pp 76 to 78.

Teaching sequence

6

a

- Ask pupils to work in pairs to write and solve two-step word problems using the helping words and numbers.
- Guide pupils to:
  1) look at the words and think of two parts of a problem
  2) recall the concepts of division and apply them to the first part of the problem
  3) think of an addition or subtraction concept and apply it to the second part of the word problem.
- **Note**: Pupils can use additional words other than the ones given.
- The following is an example of a two-step word problem: Tai had 450 pencils and Ruby had 260 pencils.
  (a) How many pencils did they have altogether?
  (b) If the pencils were shared equally between Tai and Ruby, how many pencils did each of them get?
- **Note**: The 'part-whole' concept (addition) and division concept (finding the number of items in each group) are applied in the example.

b

- Help pupils to relate the model to the four operation concepts. Make a list of the concepts to help them choose the correct one.

7 *Put On Your Thinking Caps!*

a

- Pupils should read and interpret the problem and relate it to the model. Then fill in the unknown values to solve the problem.

b

- Pupils should use 'guess and check' to solve the problem.

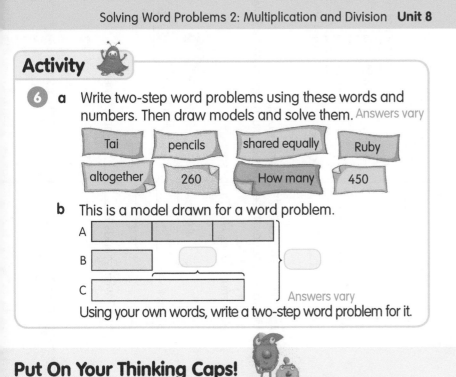

Solving Word Problems 2: Multiplication and Division **Unit 8**

Activity

6 **a** Write two-step word problems using these words and numbers. Then draw models and solve them. Answers vary

| Tai | pencils | shared equally | Ruby |
| altogether | 260 | How many | 450 |

b This is a model drawn for a word problem.

A

B

C

Answers vary

Using your own words, write a two-step word problem for it.

Put On Your Thinking Caps!

7 **a** Farmer Brown has a total of 19 geese, chickens and ducks on her farm. She has 3 more chickens than geese. She has 2 fewer ducks than geese.
How many ducks does she have? 4 ducks

Use this model to help you solve the problem.

chickens
geese
ducks
2
3
19

b Ravi fits wheels on to 21 bicycles and tricycles.
He uses 53 wheels altogether.
How many tricycles does Ravi have?
21 × 2 = 42
53 − 42 = 11
Ravi has 11 tricycles.

Practice Book 3B, p.77   Practice Book 3B, p.78   123

Unit 8

Solving Word Problems 2: Multiplication and Division

Date: _____

Practice 1

Multiplication: one-step word problems

Solve these word problems.
Fill in the spaces.

1 Cafe A sells 480 cups of tea.
Cafe B sells twice as many cups of tea as Cafe A.
How many cups of tea does Cafe B sell?

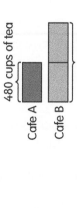

480 cups of tea

Cafe A

Cafe B

? cups of tea

$480 \times 2 =$ ___960___

Cafe B sells ___960___ cups of tea.

2 Mr Davies spends £825 on a new bed.
Mrs Taylor spends three times as much money as Mr Davies
on her new bed.
How much does Mrs Taylor spend?

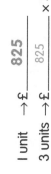

£825

Mr Davies

Mrs Taylor

£?

1 unit → £ **825**

3 units → £ 825 × 3

  = £ 2475

Mrs Taylor spends £ ___2475___ on her new bed.

Practice 2 **Multiplication: two-step word problems**

Solve these word problems.
Fill in the boxes, spaces and circles.

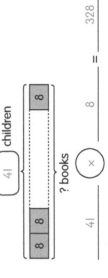

1. There are 16 boys and 25 girls in a class.
   Each child has 8 books.

   a How many children are there in the class?

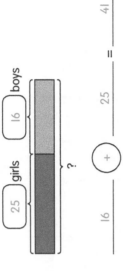

   25 girls   16 boys

   ?

   16 + 25 = 41

   There are ___41___ children in the class.

   b How many books do they have altogether?

   41 children

   8 8   8 8

   ? books

   41 × 8 = 328

   They have ___328___ books altogether.

---

3. George saves £645.
   Anna saves 4 times that amount.
   How much does Anna save?
   Draw a model and fill in the spaces.

   £645
   George
   Anna   £?

   £645 × 4 = £2580

   Anna saves £ ___2580___ .

4. A newsagent collects 236 bundles of old newspapers
   for recycling.
   A supermarket collects 5 times the number of bundles that the
   newsagent collects.
   How many bundles of old newspapers does the
   supermarket collect?
   Draw a model to solve this problem.

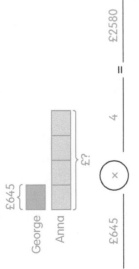

   236 bundles
   newsagent
   supermarket
   ? bundles

   1 unit → 236 bundles
   5 units → 236 × 5
           = 1180 bundles

   The supermarket collects 1180 bundles of old newspapers.

Left page (62)

2 A factory makes 487 tuna sandwiches for a supermarket.
It makes 4 times as many egg sandwiches as tuna sandwiches.

a How many egg sandwiches does the factory make?

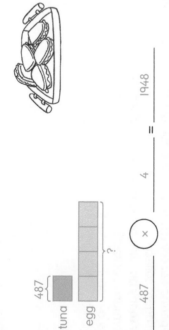

tuna 487
egg ?

487 ⊗× 4 = 1948

The factory makes **1948** egg sandwiches.

b How many more egg sandwiches than tuna sandwiches does the factory make?

tuna 487 ?
egg 1948

1948 ⊖− 487 = 1461

The factory makes **1461** more egg sandwiches than tuna sandwiches.

Right page (63)

3 A camera costs £375.
A television costs £103 more than the camera.
A laptop costs 3 times as much as the television.
How much does the laptop cost?

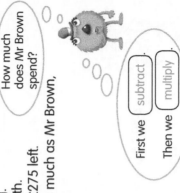

How much does the television cost?
First we [add]. Then we [multiply].

camera £375
television £375 £103 £?

£375 + £103 = £478
The television costs £478.

television £478
laptop £?

£478 × 3 = £1434
The laptop costs £1434.

4 Mr and Mrs Brown go shopping.
Mr Brown has £450 to begin with.
After shopping, Mr Brown has £275 left.
If Mrs Brown spends 4 times as much as Mr Brown, how much does she spend?

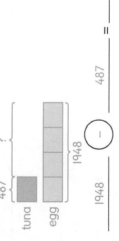

How much does Mr Brown spend?
First we [subtract]. Then we [multiply].

Mr Brown £450
£? £275

£450 − £275 = £175
Mr Brown spends £175.

Mrs Brown £175
£?

£175 × 4 = £700
She spends £700.

5 86 girls and 76 boys are in the school play.
Each child has 5 lines to say.
How many lines are in the play altogether?

86 + 76 = 162
There are 162 children altogether.

162 × 5 = 810
There are 810 lines in the play altogether.

6 Kerry has 5 boxes of books.
Each box contains 120 books.
She gives 174 books to charity.
How many books does Kerry have left?

120 × 5 = 600
There are 600 books altogether.

600 – 174 = 426
Kerry has 426 books left.

7 Some children raise money for charity.
Millie raises 5 times as much money as Ruby.
Peter raises £30 more than Millie.
Ruby raises £25.
How much money does Peter raise?

1 unit → £ __25__

5 units → 5 $\times$ 25 = £ __125__

£ __125__ = £ __125__

Millie raises £ __125__ .

£ __125__ + £ __30__ = £ __155__

Peter raises £ __155__ .

Practice 3   Division: one-step word problems

Solve these word problems.
Fill in the boxes, spaces and circles.

1. The florist has 728 flowers.
She uses 4 flowers to make a bunch.
How many bunches can she make with all the flowers?

728 flowers

4   4   4

? bunches

728 ÷ 4 = 182

She can make ___182___ bunches.

2. Miss Taylor shares 425 marbles equally between 5 children.
How many marbles does each child get?

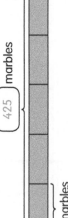

425 marbles

? marbles

425 ÷ 5 = 85

Each child gets ___85___ marbles.

8. Jack has 28 cars in his toy collection.
Omar has 4 times as many toy cars as Jack.
Ruby has 15 fewer cars than Omar.
How many cars does Ruby have?

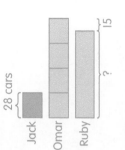

28 cars

Jack

Omar

Ruby

?

15

1 unit → 28
4 units → 4 × 28 = 112
Omar has 112 cars.

112 − 15 = 97
Ruby has 97 cars.

Date: _____

Practice 4 · Division: one-step word problems

Solve these word problems.
Fill in the boxes, spaces and circles.

1 Jack's class raises £85 for two charities.
Charity A gets 4 times as much money as Charity B.
How much does Charity B get?

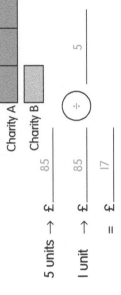

Charity A

Charity B

£ 85

5 units → £ 85

1 unit → £ 85 ÷ 5

= £ 17

Charity B gets £ 17 .

2 Mrs Roberts pours 24 cups of tea. She puts them on to a round tray and a square tray.
There are twice as many cups of tea on the square tray as on the round tray.
How many more cups of tea are there on the square tray than on the round tray?

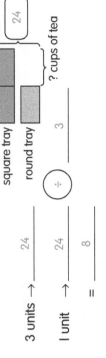

square tray

round tray

24 cups of tea

? cups of tea

3 units → 24

1 unit → 24 ÷ 3

= 8

There are 8 more cups of tea on the square tray.

Unit 8: Solving Word Problems 2: Multiplication and Division

69

---

3 Millie's cat sleeps for 84 hours in 7 days.
He sleeps an equal number of hours each day.
How many hours does Millie's cat sleep each day?

84 hours

? hours

84 ÷ 7 = 12

Millie's cat sleeps for 12 hours each day.

4 The tailor has 368 buttons and some shirts.
He sews 8 buttons on each shirt.
He sews all the buttons onto shirts.
How many shirts are there?

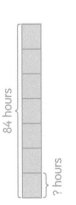

368 buttons

8 8 8

? shirts

368 ÷ 8 = 46

There are 46 shirts.

Unit 8: Solving Word Problems 2: Multiplication and Division

68

Answers Unit 8: Solving Word Problems 2: Multiplication and Division   **223**

Practice 5 Division: two-step word problems

Solve these word problems.
Fill in the boxes, spaces and circles.

1 The baker makes 643 fruit tarts.
She sells 247 fruit tarts.
She packs the remaining tarts equally into 6 containers.

a How many fruit tarts does she pack into containers?

643 fruit tarts

247 fruit tarts

? fruit tarts

643 — 247 = 396

She packs _____ 396 _____ fruit tarts into containers.

b How many fruit tarts are there in each container?

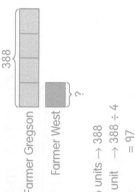

396 fruit tarts

? fruit tarts

396 ÷ 6 = 66

There are _____ 66 _____ fruit tarts in each container.

3 A carpenter fits 420 doors in a month.
He fits 3 times as many red doors as blue doors.
How many blue doors does he fit?

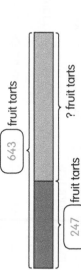

blue ?

red

420

4 units → 420
1 unit → 420 ÷ 4
= 105

He fits 105 blue doors.

4 Farmer Gregson picks 388 pears from his orchard.
He picks 4 times as many pears as Farmer West.
How many pears does Farmer West pick?

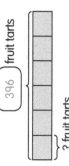

Farmer Gregson

388

Farmer West

?

4 units → 388
1 unit → 388 ÷ 4
= 97

Farmer West picks 97 pears.

2 A shopkeeper has 844 apples.
She packs them into bags of 4 each.
She sells all the apples for £2 a bag.
How much money does the shopkeeper make?

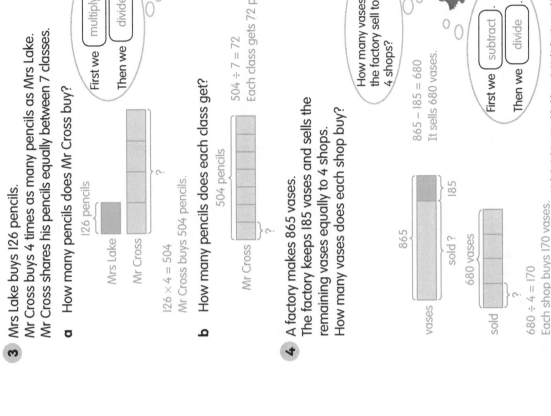

844 apples

How many bags of apples are there altogether?

844 ÷ 4 = 211

There are 211 bags of apples.

First we divide.
Then we multiply.

211 bags

£2 £2 £2 £?

211 × 2 = 422

The shopkeeper makes £422.

3 Mrs Lake buys 126 pencils.
Mr Cross buys 4 times as many pencils as Mrs Lake.
Mr Cross shares his pencils equally between 7 classes.

a How many pencils does Mr Cross buy?

126 pencils
Mrs Lake
Mr Cross
?

126 × 4 = 504
Mr Cross buys 504 pencils.

First we multiply.
Then we divide.

b How many pencils does each class get?

504 pencils
Mr Cross
?

504 ÷ 7 = 72
Each class gets 72 pencils.

4 A factory makes 865 vases.
The factory keeps 185 vases and sells the remaining vases equally to 4 shops.
How many vases does each shop buy?

vases
865
sold ?
185

865 − 185 = 680
It sells 680 vases.

How many vases does the factory sell to the 4 shops?

First we subtract.
Then we divide.

680 vases
sold
?

680 ÷ 4 = 170
Each shop buys 170 vases.

5 Daniel has £900 in savings.
He has 5 times as much money as Michael.
Isabel has £375.
How much more money does Isabel have than Michael?

First we divide .
Then we subtract .

£900 ÷ 5 = £180
Michael has £180.

£375 − £180 = £195
Isabel has £195 more than Michael.

6 Farha has 459 beads.
She has 286 fewer beads than Miya.
Miya has 5 times as many beads as Ella.
How many beads does Ella have?

First we add .
Then we divide .

459 + 286 = 745
Miya has 745 beads.

745 ÷ 5 = 149
Ella has 149 beads.

7 A baker makes 328 buns.
He then makes another 64 buns.
He packs all the buns equally into 8 identical boxes.
How many buns are there in each box?

328 buns   64 buns
? buns

328 + 64 = 392
392 buns

? buns
392 ÷ 8 = 49
There are 49 buns in each box.

8 Mr Brown saves £760 each month.
Mr Green saves £490 each month.
How much more does Mr Brown save than Mr Green after 8 months?

£760
Mr Brown
Mr Green
£490   £?

£760 − £490 = £270

£?
£270 £270   £270
8 months

£270 × 8 = £2160
Mr Brown saves £2160 more than Mr Green after 8 months.

Maths Journal

1. Use the models, number sentences and the answer statement below to help you write a word problem.

89 patients

Dr Taylor
Dr Harris

? patients
? patients
? patients

Method 1

$89 \times 2 = 178$
$178 + 89 = 267$

or

Method 2

1 unit → 89
3 units → 3 × 89
          = 267

The two doctors have 267 patients altogether.

My word problem is:

[ ]

Answers vary.
Example:
Dr Taylor has 89 patients.
Dr Harris has twice as many patients as Dr Taylor.
How many patients do the two doctors have altogether?

Challenging Practice

Solve this word problem.

1. Jack and Peter have 24 marbles altogether. After Jack gives Peter 5 marbles, they have the same number of marbles. How many marbles did Peter have to begin with?

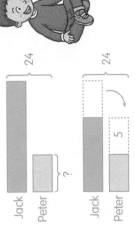

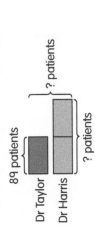

Jack
Peter
24
?

Jack
Peter
24
5

$24 \div 2 = 12$
$12 - 5 = 7$
Peter had 7 marbles to begin with.

Problem Solving

I Ruby has some beads and 6 pieces of thread.
She threads 3 beads on to each piece of thread.
She has 2 beads left.

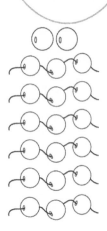

3 beads on each piece
of thread.
There are 6 pieces of thread.
$6 \times 3 = 18$
This means there are
18 beads on 6 pieces
of thread.

If she threads 4 beads on to each piece of thread:

a how many beads are left?

b how many pieces of thread does she need?

a 18 + 2 = 20
20 ÷ 4 = 5
No beads are left.

b She needs 5 pieces of thread.

Unit 8: Solving Word Problems 2: Multiplication and Division

78

Week	Learning Objectives	Thinking Skills	Resources
7	**(1) Mental addition** Pupils will be able to: • add a 2-digit number to another 2-digit number mentally using the 'add tens followed by add ones' strategy (for tens without regrouping) • add a 2-digit number to another 2-digit number mentally using the 'add tens and subtract a number' strategy (for tens with regrouping)	• Comparing numbers • Applying number bonds	• Pupil Textbook 3A, pp 124 to 126 • Practice Book 3B, pp 79 to 80 • Teacher's Guide 3A, pp 232 to 234
7	**(2) Mental subtraction** Pupils will be able to: • subtract a 2-digit number from another 2-digit number using the 'subtract tens followed by subtract ones' strategy (for minuend with ones greater than the ones of the subtrahend) • subtract a 2-digit number from another 2-digit number using the 'subtract tens and add a number' strategy (for minuend with ones smaller than the ones of the subtrahend)	• Comparing numbers • Applying number bonds	• Pupil Textbook 3A, pp 127 to 128 • Practice Book 3B, pp 81 to 84 • Teacher's Guide 3A, pp 235 to 236

Unit 9: Mental Calculations

Week	Learning Objectives	Thinking Skills	Resources
7	**(3) More mental addition** Pupils will be able to: • add a 2-digit number close to 100 to another 2-digit number using the 'add 100 and subtract a number' strategy • add two 2-digit numbers that are both close to 100, using the 'add 200 and subtract two numbers' strategy	• Comparing numbers • Applying number bonds	• Pupil Textbook 3A, pp 129 to 131 • Practice Book 3B, pp 85 to 86 • Teacher's Guide 3A, pp 237 to 239
7	**(4) Mental multiplication** Pupils will be able to: • use the commutative property as a pattern to find a multiplication fact • break up a large number with tens to a single digit number and tens to find the multiplication	• Applying number bonds	• Pupil Textbook 3A, pp 132 to 133 • Practice Book 3B, pp 87 to 88 • Teacher's Guide 3A, pp 240 to 241

Unit 9: Mental Calculations

Medium-term plan

Week	Learning Objectives	Thinking Skills	Resources
7	**(5) Mental division**		• Pupil Textbook 3A, pp 134 to 136
	Pupils will be able to:		• Practice Book 3B, pp 89 to 92
	• find division facts by first recalling related multiplication facts		• Teacher's Guide 3A, pp 242 to 244
	• break up a large number with tens to a single digit number and tens to find the division		
	Let's Explore!		
	Pupils will be able to relate and connect numbers and operators to make multiplication and division sentences.		
	Review 4 Revision 2		• Practice Book 3B, pp 93 to 104

Summative assessment opportunities

Assessment Book 3, Test 4, pp 31 to 36
For extension, Assessment Book 3, Challenging Problems 2, pp 37 to 38
Assessment Book 3, Check-up 2, pp 39 to 48

Mental Calculations

Learning objectives: Mental addition

Pupils will be able to:

- add a 2-digit number to another 2-digit number mentally using the 'add tens followed by add ones' strategy (for tens without regrouping)

- add a 2-digit number to another 2-digit number mentally using the 'add tens and subtract a number' strategy (for tens with regrouping)

Key concept

Applying number bonds to assist mental calculations

Teaching sequence

- Revise place values for whole numbers involving tens and ones and number bonds representing 2-digit numbers.
- Explain that 52 is the same as 5 tens and 2 ones or 50 and 2.
- Explain one strategy for mental calculation is to **add from left to right**. The strategy is to add the tens followed by the ones. Work through the example in the textbook:
  34 + 52 = ___
  First add 5 tens to 34
  → 8 tens and 4 = 84
  Next add 2 ones to 84 → 86
  Invite volunteers to work through the procedure above. Ask them to say the steps to find 34 + 52 using mental calculation.

- Ask pupils to work out the answer to this question on a piece of paper using the procedure in ❶.
- Pupils are expected to recall the steps for a mental calculation as follows:
  45 + 23 = ___
  45 plus 2 tens = 65 (they may skip the step 6 tens 5 ones)
  65 plus 3 ones = 68

Unit 9 Mental Calculations

Let's Learn!

Mental addition

① What is 34 + 52?

52 = (5) tens (2) ones

$$34 + 50 = 84$$
$$\downarrow$$
$$34 + 52 = 84 + 2$$
$$= 86$$
$$34 + 52 = 86$$

First we add 5 tens to 34.

Then we add 2 ones to 84.

② What is 45 + 23?

23 = (2) tens (3) ones

$$45 + 20 = (65)$$
$$\downarrow$$
$$45 + 23 = (65) + 3$$
$$= (68)$$

First we add 2 tens to 45.

Then we add 3 ones to (65).

124

- Comparing numbers
- Applying number bonds

Additional activity

Work through the following number bond strategy and ask pupils to commit to memory:

- Adding 49 is the same as adding 50 minus 1
- Adding 48 is the same as adding 50 minus 2
- Adding 47 is the same as adding 50 minus 3
- Adding 46 is the same as adding 50 minus 4

Mental Calculations **Unit 9**

3 What is 34 + 48?

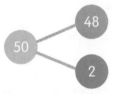

34 + 50 = 84
↓
34 + 48 = 84 − 2
= 82
34 + 48 = 82

First we add 50 to 34.

Then we subtract 2 from 84.

Do you know why we add 50 and then subtract 2?

4 What is 35 + 47?

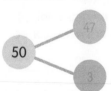

35 + 50 = (85)
↓
35 + 47 = (85) − (3)
= (82)
35 + 47 = (82)

First we add 50 to 35.

Then we subtract (3) from (85).

Home Maths
Tell your child that these are some ways of adding two numbers to make 50.
50 = 41 + 9   50 = 43 + 7   50 = 45 + 5   50 = 47 + 3   50 = 49 + 1
42 + 8 = 50   44 + 6 = 50   46 + 4 = 50   48 + 2 = 50

125

Teaching sequence

3

- Explain to pupils that the earlier questions are addition of numbers without regrouping. The following will involve regrouping.
- Explain the following steps of the strategy:

  First step: Look at the numbers and select one which is near a ten.
  In this example, 48 is near 50.

  Second step: Think of a number bond.
  50 → 2 and 48

  Third step: Use this strategy: adding 48 is the same as adding 50 and minus 2.

  Fourth step:
  34 plus 50 → 84
  84 minus 2 → 82

4

- Ask pupils to work in pairs to work out: 35 + 47
  They should realise that adding 47 is the same as adding 50 and minus 3.

Unit 9: Mental Calculations   **233**

Independent work

Practice I in Practice Book 3B, pp 79 to 80.

Additional activity

Ask pupils to work in pairs. Pupil A says a number with its ones digit near a ten, e.g., 28, 37, 49, 78. They then ask, "*What is 37?*" Pupil B replies: "*37 is 40 minus 3.*" Pupils A and B swap roles.

Teaching sequence

5 *Game*

- The objective of this activity is to encourage pupils to work on various types of addition problems involving two 2-digit numbers and to reinforce the strategies they have just learnt.

Game

5 **Let's add mentally!**

How to play:

Players: 2 to 4
You will need:
- cards with numbers from 46 to 55

I   Player I calls out a number between I0 and I00.

2   Player I then picks a card.

3   Player I adds the two numbers mentally and tells the other players their answer.

4   The other players check the answer.
Player I gets I point if their answer is correct.

5   Return the card to the pack and shuffle it.
Take turns to play.
Play three rounds each.

The player with the most points wins!

Practice Book 3B, p.79

126

Pupils will be able to:

- subtract a 2-digit number from another 2-digit number using the 'subtract tens followed by subtract ones' strategy (for minuend with ones greater than the ones of the subtrahend)
- subtract a 2-digit number from another 2-digit number using the 'subtract tens and add a number' strategy (for minuend with ones smaller than the ones of the subtrahend)

Key concept

Applying number bonds in subtraction

Thinking skills

- Comparing numbers
- Applying number bonds

Mental Calculations **Unit 9**

Let's Learn!

Mental subtraction

1 What is 87 – 34?

$34 = \boxed{3}$ tens $\boxed{4}$ ones

87 – 30 = 57
↓
87 – 34 = 57 – 4
　　　　= 53
87 – 34 = 53

> First we subtract 3 tens from 87.
>
> Then we subtract 4 ones from 57.

2 What is 79 – 45?

$45 = \boxed{4}$ tens $\boxed{5}$ ones

$79 - \boxed{40} = \boxed{39}$
↓
$79 - 45 = \boxed{39} - 5$
　　　　$= \boxed{34}$
$79 - 45 = \boxed{34}$

> First we subtract $\boxed{4}$ tens from 79.
>
> Then we subtract 5 ones from $\boxed{39}$.

127

Teaching sequence

1

- Explain that 34 is the same as 3 tens and 4 ones or 30 and 4.
- Explain one strategy for mental subtraction is to **subtract from left to right**.
- The strategy is to subtract the tens, followed by the ones.
- Work through the example in the textbook:
  87 – 34 = ___
- First subtract 3 tens from 87 → 5 tens and 7 = 57 Next subtract 4 ones from 57 → 53
- Invite volunteers to work through the procedure above.
- Ask pupils to explain the steps to find 87 – 34 using mental calculation.

2

- Ask pupils to complete this question on a piece of paper. Ask them to solve the same question mentally using the procedure in **1**.
- Pupils are expected to recall the steps for mental calculation as follows:
  79 – 45 = ___
  79 minus 4 tens = 39
  39 minus 5 ones = 34

- Work through the following number bond strategy and ask pupils to commit to memory:
  - Minus 49 is the same as minus 50 plus 1
  - Minus 48 is the same as minus 50 plus 2
  - Minus 47 is the same as minus 50 plus 3
  - Minus 46 is the same as minus 50 plus 4

- Ask pupils to work in pairs. Pupil A says a number with its ones digit near a ten, e.g., 28, 37, 49. Then they ask, "*What is minus 37?*" Pupil B replies: "*minus 37 is minus 40 add 3.*" Pupils should then swap roles.

Independent work

Practice 2 in Practice Book 3B, pp 81 to 84.

Teaching sequence

- Explain to pupils that the earlier questions are subtraction of numbers without regrouping.
- This example will involve regrouping. However, in mental calculation, we do not use regrouping to find the answer, but a special strategy.
- Explain the following steps of the strategy:

  First step: Look at the numbers and select one that is near a ten.
  In this example, 48 is near 50.

  Second step: Think of a number bond.
  50 → 2 and 48

  Third step: Use this strategy: minus 48 is the same as minus 50 and add 2.

  Fourth step:
  63 minus 50 → 13
  13 plus 2 → 15

- Ask pupils to work in pairs to work out: 72 – 47.
- They should realise that subtracting 47 is the same as subtracting 50 and adding 3.

Unit 9 Mental Calculations

 What is 63 – 48?

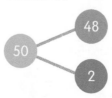

63 – 50 = 13
↓
63 – 48 = 13 + 2
= 15
63 – 48 = 15

First we subtract 50 from 63.

Then we add 2 to 13.

Do you know why we subtract 50 and then add 2?

④ What is 72 – 47?

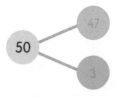

72 – 50 = (22)
↓
72 – 47 = (22) + 3
= (25)
72 – 47 = 25

First we subtract 50 from 72.

Then we add (3) to (22).

Practice Book 3B, p.81

 Play the game on page 126 with your child. One of you calls out a number between 56 and 100. Continue with the game using steps **2**, **4** and **5**. For step **3**, subtract the smaller number from the greater number mentally.

128

Learning objectives: More mental addition

Pupils will be able to:

- add a 2-digit number close to 100 to another 2-digit number using the 'add 100 and subtract a number' strategy
- add two 2-digit numbers that are both close to 100, using the 'add 200 and subtract two numbers' strategy

Key concept

Relating a number that is close to 100 to a number bond and applying the number bond to do mental addition

Thinking skills

- Comparing numbers
- Applying number bonds

Additional activity

Work through the following 'number bond' strategy and ask pupils to commit to memory:

- Add 99 is the same as add 100 minus 1
- Add 98 is the same as add 100 minus 2
- Add 97 is the same as add 100 minus 3
- Add 96 is the same as add 100 minus 4

Teaching sequence

1

- Explain to pupils that this question involves addition of numbers with regrouping. However, in mental calculation, we do not use regrouping.
- Explain the following steps of the strategy:

  First step: Look at the numbers and select one that is near a ten. In this example, 95 is near 100.

  Second step: Think of a number bond.
  100 → 95 and 5

  Third step: Use this strategy: adding 95 is the same as adding 100 and minus 5.

  Fourth step:
  86 plus 100 → 186
  186 minus 5 → 181

2

- Ask pupils to work in pairs to work on this question: 75 + 98. They should realise that adding 98 is the same as adding 100 and minus 2.

Mental Calculations **Unit 9**

Let's Learn!

More mental addition

1 What is 86 + 95?

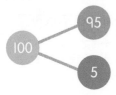

$86 + 100 = 186$
$\downarrow$
$86 + 95 = 186 - 5$
$\quad = 181$
$86 + 95 = 181$

First we add 100 to 86.

Then we subtract 5 from 186.

Do you know why we add 100 and then subtract 5?

2 What is 75 + 98?

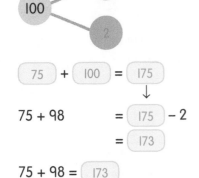

$\boxed{75} + \boxed{100} = \boxed{175}$
$\downarrow$
$75 + 98 \quad = \boxed{175} - 2$
$\quad = \boxed{173}$
$75 + 98 = \boxed{173}$

First we add 100 to 75.

Then we subtract $\boxed{2}$ from $\boxed{175}$.

129

What you will need
- Base ten equipment
- Place value charts

Teaching sequence

- Explain to pupils that in this question, the two addends are each close to 100. The following strategy is used.

  First step: Think of two number bonds.
  100 → 94 and 6
  100 → 97 and 3

  Second step: Use this strategy: adding 94 is the same as adding 100 and minus 6. Adding 97 is the same as adding 100 and minus 3.

  Third step: Add the 200 and minus 6 and then minus 3, i.e., 200 − 6 − 3 = 191

- Ask pupils to work on this question in pairs: 95 + 99. They should realise that adding 95 is the same as adding 100 and minus 5 and adding 99 is the same as adding 100 and minus 1.

Unit 9 Mental Calculations

③ What is 94 + 97?

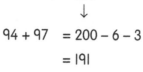

94 and 97 are each near 100.

100 + 100 = 200
↓
94 + 97 = 200 − 6 − 3
= 191
94 + 97 = 191

First we add the hundreds.

Then we subtract 6 and 3 from 200.

④ What is 95 + 99?

95 and 99 are each near 100.

100 + 100 = [200]
↓
95 + 99 = [200] − 5 − 1
= [194]
95 + 99 = [194]

First we add the hundreds.

Then we subtract the ones from [200].

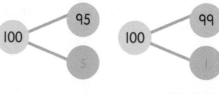
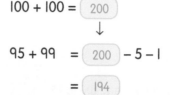

Home Maths Tell your child that these are some ways of adding two numbers to make 100.
100 = 91 + 9   100 = 93 + 7   100 = 95 + 5   100 = 97 + 3   100 = 99 + 1
92 + 8 = 100   94 + 6 = 100   96 + 4 = 100   98 + 2 = 100

130

Independent work

Practice 3 in Practice Book 3B, pp 85 to 86.

What you will need

- A dice
- Cards with numbers 92 to 99

Game

5 **More mental addition!**

How to play:

Players: 2 to 5
You will need:
- a dice
- cards with numbers 92 to 99

1 Player 1 rolls the dice twice to make a 2-digit number.

2 Player 1 picks a card to get another number.

3 Player 1 adds the two numbers mentally and tells the other players their answer.

65 + 99 = 164

4 The other players check the answer. Player 1 gets 1 point if their answer is correct.

5 Return the card to the pack and shuffle the cards. Take turns to play. Play three rounds each.

The player with the most points wins!

Practice Book 3B, p.85

131

Teaching sequence

5 *Game*

- The objective of the game is to allow pupils to practise using the strategy explained in the earlier sections.
- Prepare number cards from 92 to 99. Pupils should obtain other sets of numbers below 70 by rolling the dice.
- **Note**: The dice can be modified to include other numbers by sticking on additional numbers such as 7, 8 or 9.

Learning objectives: Mental multiplication

Pupils will be able to:

- use the commutative property as a pattern to find a multiplication fact
- break up a large number with tens to a single digit number and tens to find the multiplication

Key concept

Reversing the order of groups and items in a multiplication concept produces the same product.

Thinking skill

Applying number bonds

Teaching sequence

- Explain the commutative rule in multiplication. Apply this to the example given in the textbook.
- Pupils need to know that 3 × 4 is the same as 4 × 3.
- The two multiplication facts can be illustrated using dot paper to show that they are the same.

- Encourage pupils to recognise that this example can be tackled using the above method.
- Ask pupils to find the answer.

- Explain that some multiplications can be tackled by recalling and relating them to multiplication facts.
- To find 5 × 40 and 5 × 400, pupils need to relate and recall 5 × 4.
- If 5 × 4 = 20, then 5 × 40 = 200 and 5 × 400 = 2000

Let's Learn!

Mental multiplication

① What is 4 × 3?

4 × 3 = 12

Skip-count in threes. 3, 6, 9, 12.

What is 3 × 4 = ?

3 × 4 = 12

3 × 4 is the same as 4 × 3.

② What is 4 × 6?

6 × 4 = [24]

4 × 6 = [24]

4 × 6 is the same as 6 × 4.

③ What is 5 × 40?
What is 5 × 400?

×	4	40	400
5	20	200	2000

5 × 4 = 20

5 × 40 = 5 × 4 tens = 20 tens
　　　　　　　　　　　　= 200

5 × 40 = 200

Can you see a pattern?

5 × 400 = 5 × 4 hundreds = 20 hundreds
　　　　　　　　　　　　　　　= 2000

5 × 400 = 2000

Tell your child that these are some tips for remembering multiplication facts.
There is a pattern for 12 = 3 × 4 and 56 = 7 × 8.

1, 2, 3, 4　　　5, 6, 7, 8
12 = 3 × 4　　　56 = 7 × 8

Home Maths

132

Independent work
Practice 4 in Practice Book 3B, pp 87 to 88.

Mental Calculations **Unit 9**

4 What is 6 × 70?
What is 6 × 700?

6 × 70 = 6 × [7] tens

= [42] tens

= [420]

6 × 70 = [420]

6 × 700 = 6 × [7] hundreds

= [42] hundreds

= [4200]

6 × 700 = [4200]

5 Multiply mentally.

a   8 × 60 = [480]

b   9 × 400 = [3600]

8 × 6 = [48]

8 × 60 = [480]

9 × 4 = [36]

9 × 400 = [3600]

Teaching sequence

4

- Encourage pupils to recognise that this example can be tackled using the above pattern. Remind them of the place value concept. 70 is 7 tens and 700 is 7 hundreds.
- Ask pupils to find the answer.

5

- Ask pupils to complete these mental calculations.

 Practise mental multiplication with your child when you are out shopping. For example, a mug costs £3. How much would 6 mugs cost?

Practice Book 3B, p.87

Learning objectives: Mental division

Pupils will be able to:

- find division facts by first recalling related multiplication facts
- break up a large number with tens to a single digit number and tens to find the division

Key concept

Division is the inverse of multiplication.

Additional activities

- Ask pupils to work in pairs. Pupil A writes a multiplication fact. Pupil B writes a related multiplication fact and two related division facts. Pupils A and B swap roles.
- Ask pupils to work in pairs. Pupil A writes a division fact. Pupil B writes a related multiplication fact and finds the answer. Pupils A and B swap roles.

Teaching sequence

- Explain and recall multiplication and division concepts. Demonstrate how they are related. Use models to show their relationship.
- Multiplication: given the multiplier and multiplicand, find the total number.
- Division: given the total and the multiplier or multiplicand, find the multiplicand or multiplier.
- Relate this concept to the strategy used to divide mentally.
- Pupils need to have mastered their times tables before they can do mental division.
- Strategy: recall a related multiplication fact to find a division fact.
  $24 ÷ 6 = 4$, $24 ÷ 4 = 6$
  $6 × 4 = 24$, $4 × 6 = 24$
  All these are related facts.

- Encourage pupils to recognise that these examples can be tackled using the above strategy by relating division and multiplication facts.
- Ask pupils to find the answer.

Unit 9 Mental Calculations

Let's Learn!

Mental division

① What is $24 ÷ 6$?

$24 ÷ 6 = 4$

> Think of the 6 times table.
> $4 × 6 = 24$

② What is $35 ÷ 7$?

$35 ÷ 7 = \boxed{5}$

> Think of the 7 or 5 times table.
> $5 × 7 = 35$
> $5 × \boxed{7} = 35$

③ What is $63 ÷ 9$?

$63 ÷ 9 = \boxed{7}$

> Think of the 9 times table.
> $7 × 9 = 63$

④ What is $32 ÷ 8$?

$32 ÷ 8 = \boxed{4}$

> Think of the 8 times table.
> $4 × 8 = 32$

> **Home Maths** Encourage your child to memorise the times tables. Division is easier when they know the times tables.

134

Additional activity

Ask pupils to work in pairs. Pupil A calls out a division fact. Pupil B calls out the answer. Pupils take turns to call out the questions and say the correct answers.

5 What is 80 ÷ 4?
What is 800 ÷ 4?

80 ÷ 4 = 8 tens ÷ 4
       = 2 tens
       = 20
80 ÷ 4 = 20

800 ÷ 4 = 8 hundreds ÷ 4
         = 2 hundreds
         = 200
800 ÷ 4 = 200

Use the 4 times table.
$2 \times 4 = 8$
$8 \div 4 = 2$

÷	8	80	800
4	2	20	200

6 What is 42 ÷ 6?
What is 420 ÷ 6?
What is 4200 ÷ 6?

42 ÷ 6 = ⟨ 42 ⟩ ones ÷ 6
     = ⟨ 7 ⟩ ones
     = ⟨ 7 ⟩
42 ÷ 6 = ⟨ 7 ⟩

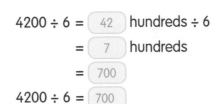

Use the 6 times table.
⟨ 7 ⟩ × 6 = 42
42 ÷ 6 = ⟨ 7 ⟩

420 ÷ 6 = ⟨ 42 ⟩ tens ÷ 6
      = ⟨ 7 ⟩ tens
      = ⟨ 70 ⟩
420 ÷ 6 = ⟨ 70 ⟩

4200 ÷ 6 = ⟨ 42 ⟩ hundreds ÷ 6
       = ⟨ 7 ⟩ hundreds
       = ⟨ 700 ⟩
4200 ÷ 6 = ⟨ 700 ⟩

135

Teaching sequence

5

- Explain that some divisions can be tackled by recalling and relating to division facts.
- To find 800 ÷ 4 = 200, first recall that 8 divided by 4 is 2. Therefore, 8 hundreds divided by 4 gives 2 hundreds.

6

- Encourage pupils to recognise that this example can be tackled using the above pattern. Remind them of the place value concept. 420 is 42 tens and 4200 is 42 hundreds.
- Ask pupils to find the answer.

Teaching sequence

7 and **8**

- Ask pupils to complete these questions.

9 *Let's Explore!*

- Guide pupils to relate three numbers that can make four related facts. Pupils may resort to the 'guess and check' method.
- Pupils can choose two numbers and find the third number. For example, they can choose any two numbers and try to find out if a third number can be found from the list.
- E.g., I choose 4 and 7. I know 4 × 7 = 28. Do we have 28 in the list? Yes. So 4 × 7 = 28, 7 × 4 = 28, 28 ÷ 7 = 4 and 28 ÷ 4 = 7

Pupils will be able to relate and connect numbers and operators to make multiplication and division sentences

Independent work

Practice 5 in Practice Book 3B, pp 89 to 92.

Unit 9 Mental Calculations

7 Find the missing numbers.

a   300 ÷ 3 = (3) hundreds ÷ 3

= (1) hundred

= (100)

b   350 ÷ 5 = (35) tens ÷ 5

= (7) tens

= (70)

8 Divide mentally.

a   700 ÷ 7 100   b   280 ÷ 7 40   c   560 ÷ 8 70

Practice Book 3B, p.89

Let's Explore!

9 These are some numbers drawn from a pack of cards. Use ×, ÷ and = to write down all the multiplication and division sentences you can make with these numbers.

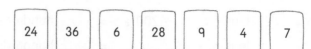

| 24 | 36 | 6 | 28 | 9 | 4 | 7 |

24 ÷ 6 = 4   36 ÷ 4 = 9   6 × 4 = 24   9 × 4 = 36
24 ÷ 4 = 6   36 ÷ 6 = 6   4 × 6 = 24   4 × 9 = 36
28 ÷ 4 = 7   36 ÷ 9 = 4   7 × 4 = 28   6 × 6 = 36
28 ÷ 7 = 4   4 × 7 = 28

136

Mental Calculations

Date: _____

Practice 1   Mental addition

First add 50.
Then add 2.

1 Fill in the spaces and circles.

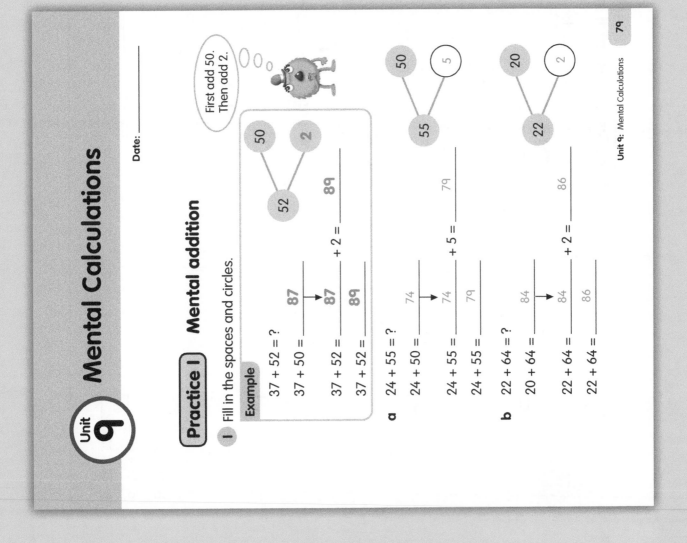

Example

37 + 52 = ?

    52
   / \
  50   2

37 + 50 = **87**

87 → 87 + 2 = **89**

37 + 52 = **89**

a 24 + 55 = ?

    55
   / \
  50   5

24 + 50 = 74

74 → 74 + 5 = 79

24 + 55 = 79

b 22 + 64 = ?

    22
   / \
  20   2

20 + 64 = 84

84 → 84 + 2 = 86

22 + 64 = 86

Practice 2   Mental subtraction

1 Fill in the spaces and circles.

Example

78 − 53 = ?

78 − 50 = **28**

78 − 53 = **28** → **28** − 3 = **25**

78 − 53 = **25**

a 89 − 57 = ?

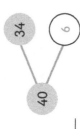

89 − 50 = 39

89 − 57 = 39 → 39 − 7 = 32

89 − 57 = 32

b 75 − 33 = ?

89 − 50 = 45

75 − 30 = 45

75 − 33 = 45 → 45 − 3 = 42

75 − 33 = 42

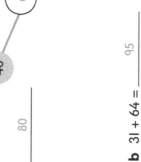

---

2 Fill in the spaces and circles.

First add 50. Then subtract 2.

a 19 + 48 = ?

19 + 50 = 69

19 + 48 = 69 → 69 − 2 = 67

19 + 48 = 67

b 37 + 45 = ?

37 + 50 = 87

37 + 45 = 87 → 87 − 5 = 82

37 + 45 = 82

c 46 + 34 = ?

46 + 40 = 86

46 + 34 = 86 → 86 − 6 = 80

46 + 34 = 80

3 Add mentally.

a 41 + 43 = 84

b 31 + 64 = 95

c 15 + 47 = 62

d 46 + 48 = 94

e 17 + 54 = 71

f 48 + 53 = 101

d 72 − 44 = ?

72 − 50 = 22

72 − 44 = 22

72 − 44 = 28

_____ + 6 = 28

e 88 − 39 = ?

88 − 40 = 48

88 − 39 = 48

88 − 39 = 49

_____ + 1 = 49

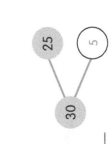

3 Add mentally.

a 84 − 23 = 61   **b** 55 − 31 = 24

c 58 − 42 = 16   **d** 79 − 65 = 14

4 Add mentally.

a 92 − 34 = 58   **b** 75 − 47 = 28

c 61 − 26 = 35   **d** 82 − 33 = 49

e 93 − 48 = 45   **f** 81 − 45 = 36

g 70 − 19 = 51   **h** 64 − 27 = 37

---

2 Fill in the spaces and circles.

Example

83 − 47 = ?

83 − 50 = **33**

83 − 47 = **33**

83 − 47 = **36**

_____ + 3 = **36**

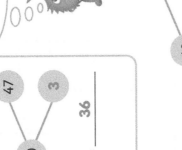

First subtract 50. Then add 3.

a 92 − 33 = ?

92 − 40 = 52

92 − 33 = 52

92 − 33 = 59

_____ + 7 = 59

b 87 − 18 = ?

87 − 20 = 67

87 − 18 = 67

87 − 18 = 69

_____ + 2 = 69

c 65 − 25 = ?

65 − 30 = 35

65 − 25 = 35

65 − 25 = 40

_____ + 5 = 40

Practice 3 More mental addition

1 Fill in the spaces and circles.

Example

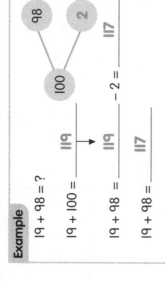

(speech bubble) First add 100. Then subtract 2.

Number bond: 100 → 98, 2

19 + 98 = ?

19 + 100 = 119

19 + 98 = 119 → 119 − 2 = 117

19 + 98 = 117

a 26 + 96 = ?

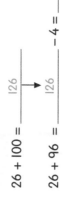   100 → 96, 4

26 + 100 = 126

26 + 96 = 126 → 126 − 4 = 122

26 + 96 = 122

b 38 + 95 = ?

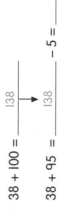   100 → 95, 5

38 + 100 = 138

38 + 95 = 138 → 138 − 5 = 133

38 + 95 = 133

---

5 Complete the puzzle. Subtract mentally.

97	−	42	=	55
−		−		
36	−	28	=	8
=		−		
61	−	19	=	42
		=		−
		9		25
				=
				17

Practice 4 Mental multiplication

Skip-count in fours.

1 Fill in the spaces.

a What is 4 × 6?

4 × 6 is the same as 6 × 4.

4 × 6 = 24

b What is 9 × 3?

9 × 3 is the same as 3 × 9.

9 × 3 = 27

c What is 7 × 5?

7 × 5 is the same as 5 × 7.

7 × 5 = 35

d What is 8 × 9?

8 × 9 is the same as 9 × 8.

8 × 9 = 72

---

2 Add mentally.

a 27 + 95 = 122 (N)

b 54 + 97 = 151 (U)

c 45 + 98 = 143 (I)

d 78 + 95 = 173 (A)

e 98 + 94 = 192 (C)

f 98 + 98 = 196 (L)

g 93 + 98 = 191 (P)

h 91 + 99 = 190 (F)

Match the letters to the numbers to find the name of a sporting event.

The	C	U	P	F	I	N	A	L
	192	151	191	190	143	122	173	196

Practice 5   Mental division

1 Think about the 6, 7, 8 and 9 times tables.
Fill in the spaces.

a $36 \div 6 = 6$ $\underset{6}{\underline{\hspace{2em}}} \times 6 = 36$

b $35 \div 7 = 5$ $\underset{5}{\underline{\hspace{2em}}} \times 7 = 35$

c $72 \div 8 = 9$ $\underset{9}{\underline{\hspace{2em}}} \times 8 = 72$

d $63 \div 9 = 7$ $\underset{7}{\underline{\hspace{2em}}} \times 9 = 63$

e $81 \div 9 = 9$ $\underset{9}{\underline{\hspace{2em}}} \times 9 = 81$

2 Multiply mentally

a $3 \times 50 = 3 \times 5$ tens
   $= \underline{15}$ tens
   $= \underline{150}$

b $3 \times 500 = 3 \times 5$ hundreds
   $= \underline{15}$ hundreds
   $= \underline{1500}$

c $7 \times 40 = 7 \times 4$ tens
   $= \underline{28}$ tens
   $= \underline{280}$

d $7 \times 400 = 7 \times 4$ hundreds
   $= \underline{28}$ hundreds
   $= \underline{2800}$

e $8 \times 60 = 8 \times 6$ tens
   $= \underline{48}$ tens
   $= \underline{480}$

f $8 \times 600 = 8 \times 6$ hundreds
   $= \underline{48}$ hundreds
   $= \underline{4800}$

g $9 \times 20 = \underline{180}$

h $9 \times 200 = \underline{1800}$

i $2 \times 70 = \underline{140}$

j $2 \times 700 = \underline{1400}$

k $8 \times 30 = \underline{240}$

l $8 \times 300 = \underline{2400}$

Maths Journal

1 Fill in the boxes to show the steps for adding mentally.
You can use the numbers more than once.
Only use the words you need.

a $35 + 48 = ?$

Step 1: Add [50] to [35] and
the answer is [85].

Step 2: Then [subtract] [2] from [85].

$35 + 48 = 83$

b $18 + 53 = ?$

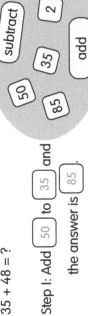

[18] + [50] = [68]

[68] + [3] = [71]

Step 1: Add [50] to [18] and the answer is [68].

Step 2: Then [add] [3] to [68].

$53 + 18 = 71$

---

2 Fill in the spaces.

a What is $56 ÷ 7$? What is $560 ÷ 7$?

$56 ÷ 7 =$ ___56___ ones ÷ 7

= ___8___ ones

= ___8___

$560 ÷ 7 =$ ___56___ tens ÷ 7

= ___8___ tens

= ___80___

b $600 ÷ 3 =$ ___6___ hundreds ÷ 3

= ___2___ hundreds

= ___200___

3 Divide mentally.

a $240 ÷ 4 =$ ___60___   **b** $400 ÷ 8 =$ ___50___

c $120 ÷ 6 =$ ___20___   **d** $250 ÷ 5 =$ ___50___

e $180 ÷ 9 =$ ___20___   **f** $140 ÷ 7 =$ ___20___

Review 4

Date: _____

1 Using the digits 1, 3 and 8, write down:

a four 3-digit **odd numbers**   **b** two 3-digit **even numbers**.

Odd Numbers	
183	813
381	831

Even Numbers
138
318

2 Divide.

a
```
      2  3 r 2
  4 ) 9  4
      8
      1  4
      1  2
         2
```

b
```
          8  5 r 3
  5 ) 4   2  8
      4   0
          2  8
          2  5
             3
```

c
```
      3  0  5
  9 ) 9  1  5
      9
      ─  0
      ─  1  5
         1  5
            0
```

3 Match the same quotients.

a (35 ÷ 5)   (100 ÷ 5)

b (102 ÷ 3)   (21 ÷ 3)

c (80 ÷ 4)   (136 ÷ 4)

---

2 Fill in the boxes to show the steps for multiplying mentally. You can use the numbers more than once.

a 8 × 80 = ?

Step 1: Multiply [8] by [8] and the answer is 64.

Step 2: 80 is equal to (8 tens) .

Step 3: 8 × (8 tens) = (64 tens)

8 × 80 = 640

(8) (8 tens)

(64 tens)

b 9 × 600 = ?

9 × 600 = 9 × [6] hundreds

= [54] hundreds

= (5400)

(9) (6) (54)

(5400) (6 hundreds)

(54 hundreds)

Write the steps here.

Step 1: Multiply [9] by [6] and the answer is 54.

Step 2: 600 is equal to (6 hundreds) .

Step 3: 9 × (6 hundreds) = (54 hundreds)

9 × 600 = 5400

4 Fill in the missing numbers.

a 83 − 48 = ?

83 − $\underline{50}$ = $\underline{33}$

83 − 48 = $\underline{33}$ + 2 = $\underline{35}$

This means 83 − 48 = $\underline{35}$.

b 54 + 97 = ?

54 + $\underline{100}$ = $\underline{154}$

54 + 97 = $\underline{154}$ − 3 = $\underline{151}$

This means 54 + 97 = $\underline{151}$.

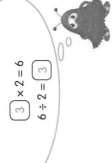

Skip-count in threes, 3, 6, 9, 12 ….

5 Multiply mentally.
Fill in the spaces.

6 × 3 = $\underline{18}$

6 × 30 = 6 × $\underline{3}$ tens
= $\underline{18}$ tens
= $\underline{180}$

6 × 300 = 6 × $\underline{3}$ hundreds
= $\underline{18}$ hundreds
= $\underline{1800}$

6 Divide mentally.
Fill in the spaces.
What is 6 ÷ 2?
What is 60 ÷ 2?
What is 600 ÷ 2?

Use the 2 times table.

$\boxed{3}$ × 2 = 6

6 ÷ 2 = $\boxed{3}$

6 ÷ 2 = $\underline{3}$

60 ÷ 2 = $\underline{6}$ tens ÷ 2
= $\underline{3}$ tens
= $\underline{30}$

600 ÷ 2 = $\underline{6}$ hundreds ÷ 2
= $\underline{3}$ hundreds
= $\underline{300}$

Solve these word problems.
Draw models to help you.

7 Peter's mum makes 125 cookies for the school fair.
Farha's dad makes three times as many cookies as Peter's mum.
How many cookies does Farha's dad make for the school fair?

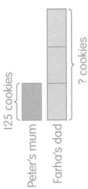

Peter's mum — 125 cookies

Farha's dad — ? cookies

125 × 3 = 375
Farha's dad makes 375 cookies for the school fair.

Revision 2

Date: _____

Section A
Choose the correct answer.
Write its letter in the box.

1. Which one of the following is **not** a number pattern?

   a 6, 12, 18, 24, 30, 36, 42, 48, 54, 60
   b 7, 14, 21, 28, 35, 42, 49, 56, 63, 70
   c 8, 16, 24, 32, 40, 48, 56, 64, 72, 80
   d 9, 18, 27, 36, 45, 54, 60, 68, 78, 90

   d

2. How many numbers between 31 and 50 can be divided exactly by 6?

   a 3   b 4
   c 6   d 10

   a

3. There are 35 children in a class.
   The children are divided into 7 equal groups.
   How many children are there in each group?

   a 7   b 6
   c 5   d 4

   c

4. Which list has all the odd numbers from 12 to 20?

   a 12, 14, 16, 18, 20   b 13, 15, 17, 19
   c 14, 16, 18   d 12, 13, 14, 15, 16

   b

---

8. Mr Taylor buys 3 boxes of oranges.
   He buys 6 boxes of apples.
   Each box contains 65 pieces of fruit.

   a How many boxes of fruit does Mr Taylor buy?

      6 boxes   3 boxes

      ?

      $3 + 6 = 9$
      Mr Taylor buys 9 boxes of fruit.

   b How many pieces of fruit does Mr Taylor buy altogether?

      9 boxes

      | 65 | 65 | | | | | | | 65 |

      ?

      $65 × 9 = 585$
      Mr Taylor buys 585 pieces of fruit altogether.

9. Miya's aunt has 375 cm of fabric to make cushions.
   She makes 4 identical cushions and has 15 cm of fabric left.
   What length of fabric is needed for each cushion?

   4 cushions   15 cm

   375 cm

   $375 − 15 = 360$
   $360 ÷ 4 = 90$
   90 cm of fabric is needed for each cushion.

5 Find the remainder when 402 is divided by 9.

a 6   b 2

c 5   d 4

a

6 What is the missing number?

5 × 7 = 35

6 × 7 = 35 + ?

a 1   b 5

c 6   d 7

d

7 To find the answer to 38 + 48, we can add 50 to:

a 38, then add 2   b 38, then subtract 2

c 48, then add 2   d 48, then subtract 2

b

8 Which one of the following is **not correct**?

a 5 × 6 = 6 + 6 + 6 + 6 + 6

b 3 × 5 = 5 × 3

c 9 × 3 = 3 + 3 + 3 + 3 + 3 + 3 + 3 + 3

d 7 × 8 = 8 + 8 + 8 + 8 + 8 + 16

d

9 What is the missing number?

```
        5 3 r 2
  ? ) 2 6 7
      2 5 0
        1 7
        1 5
           2
```

a 6   b 2

c 5   d 4

c

10 To find the answer to 8 × 900 mentally, we skip-count in:

a eights, then find 9 × 8 tens

b nines to find 8 × 9, then find 8 × 9 tens

c nines to find 8 × 9, then find 8 × 9 hundreds

d nines, then find 8 × 8 hundreds

c

Section B

11 Circle 4 groups of 7.

Read the questions and fill in the answers.

12 What is the product of 3 and 12?

36

13 84 ÷ 2 = _____ 42

14 What is the quotient when 98 is divided by 7?

14

15 Divide 250 by 5.

_50_

16 What are the missing numbers in Circle **a** and Box **b**?

$96 - 45 =$ **b**

a _5_

b _51_

17 Hardeep does this problem mentally.

$34 + 97$

First he decides to add 100 to 34.
The answer is 134.
Then he subtracts _3_ from 134.

18 The school library has 274 paperback books.
There are twice as many paperback books as hardback books.
How many hardback books are there?

_137_ hardback books

19 Tai has 6 bags of marbles.
He has 150 marbles in each bag.
How many marbles does he have?

_900_ marbles

20 Miss Smith is clearing away paintbrushes.
She puts them into 8 pots and has 12 paintbrushes left.
If there are 25 paintbrushes in each pot, how many
paintbrushes are there altogether?

_212_ paintbrushes

Section C
Read the questions.
Show your workings in the spaces provided.

21 There are 84 children on a school trip to the museum.
The children are put into 7 groups.
There are the same number of children in each group.
How many children are there in each group?

? children

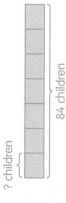

84 children

$84 \div 7 = 12$
There are 12 children in each group.

22 Millie has 60 wooden beads.
She has 5 times as many glass beads as wooden beads.
How many beads does Millie have altogether?

60 beads
wooden
glass
? beads
? beads

$60 \times 5 = 300$ or $60 \times 6 = 360$
$300 + 60 = 360$
Millie has 360 beads altogether.

23 Isabel swims 228 lengths in 6 days.
She swims the same number of lengths every day.

a How many lengths does she swim each day?

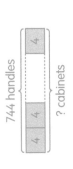

? lengths
228 lengths

$228 \div 6 = 38$
She swims 38 lengths each day.

b How many lengths will she swim in 9 days?

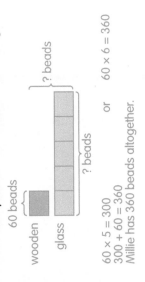

? lengths
38

$9 \times 38 = 342$
She will swim 342 lengths in 9 days.

---

24 A carpenter buys 744 handles.
He fixes 4 handles on to each cabinet.
He sells 46 cabinets.

He uses up all the handles.

a How many cabinets does he fix handles on to?

744 handles
4   4
4
? cabinets

$744 \div 4 = 186$
He fixes handles to 186 cabinets.

b How many cabinets does he have left?

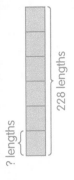

186 cabinets
left ?   46 cabinets

$186 - 46 = 140$
He has 140 cabinets left.

25 Miss Taylor buys 6 packets of stickers.
    Each packet contains 75 stickers.
    She shares the stickers equally between 9 children.
    How many stickers does each child get?

? stickers

75 stickers

$75 \times 6 = 450$
She has 450 stickers altogether.

450 stickers

? stickers

$450 \div 9 = 50$
Each child gets 50 stickers.

PHOTOCOPY MASTERS

Noogol

Googol

Koogol

Ooogol

Toogol

Zoogol

Unit I: Numbers to 10 000

Game (Pupil Textbook 3A, p 13)

Thousands	Hundreds	Tens	Ones

Unit I: Numbers to 10 000

Activity (Pupil Textbook 3A, p 20)

Thousands	Hundreds	Tens	Ones

Unit 2: Addition of Numbers within 10 000

Game (Pupil Textbook 3A, p 30)

300	600	900
200	500	800
100	400	700

Unit 3: Subtraction of Numbers within 10 000

Game (Pupil Textbook 3A, p 38)

16	36	52	42	26
20	68	26	62	10
52	88	16	36	32

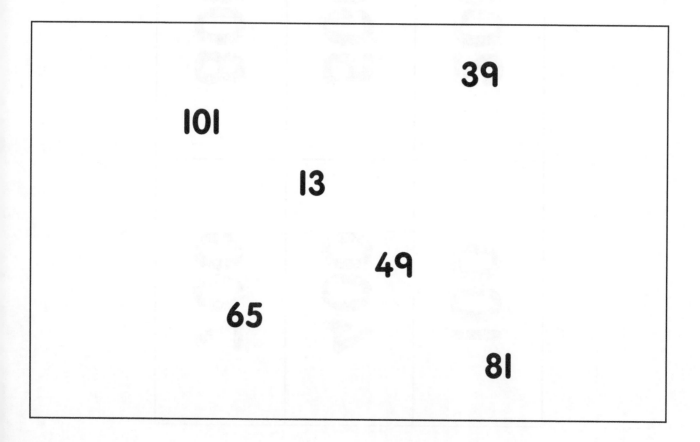

Unit 3: Subtraction of Numbers within 10 000

Game (Pupil Textbook 3A, p 49)

1	2	3
4	5	6
7	8	9
0		

Unit 3: Subtraction of Numbers within 10 000

Game (Pupil Textbook 3A, p 53)

Card A

126

12

1645

3200

Card B

1000

2000

3000

4000

Unit 5: Multiplying by 6, 7, 8 and 9

Game (Pupil Textbook 3A, p 63)

Unit 5: Multiplying by 6, 7, 8 and 9

Game (Pupil Textbook 3A, p 68)

×	1	2	3	4	5	6	7	8	9
8									
7									
6									

Unit 5: Multiplying by 6, 7, 8 and 9

Game (Pupil Textbook 3A, p 68)

6	7	8

1	2	3
4	5	6
7	8	9

Unit 5: Multiplying by 6, 7, 8 and 9

Game (Pupil Textbook 3A, p 70)

				16	12	81	24	
42				40				
21				18				
27				24				
40	45	28	63	W	30	63	36	64
				49				56
				27				48
				49				8
	36	54	14	18				

Unit 5: Multiplying by 6, 7, 8 and 9
Game (Pupil Textbook 3A, p 70)

1 × 6	2 × 6	3 × 6	4 × 6	5 × 6
6 × 6	7 × 6	8 × 6	9 × 6	10 × 6
1 × 7	2 × 7	3 × 7	4 × 7	5 × 7
6 × 7	7 × 7	8 × 7	9 × 7	10 × 7
1 × 8	2 × 8	3 × 8	4 × 8	5 × 8
6 × 8	7 × 8	8 × 8	9 × 8	10 × 8
1 × 9	2 × 9	3 × 9	4 × 9	5 × 9
6 × 9	7 × 9	8 × 9	9 × 9	10 × 9

Unit 6: Multiplication

Game (Pupil Textbook 3A, p 82)

WORKSHEET A

H	T	O	
2	2	1	
		×	

WORKSHEET B

H	T	O	
1	2	0	
		×	

WORKSHEET C

H	T	O	
1	1	2	
		×	

WORKSHEET D

H	T	O	
2	2	2	
		×	

Unit 6: Multiplication

Game! (Pupil Textbook 3A, p 87)

Question Sheet	
(a) 123 × ( ) = ( )	(b) 197 × ( ) = ( )
(c) 184 × ( ) = ( )	(d) 135 × ( ) = ( )

Question Sheet	
(a) 157 × ( ) = ( )	(b) 103 × ( ) = ( )
(c) 129 × ( ) = ( )	(d) 199 × ( ) = ( )

Question Sheet	
(a) 183 × ( ) = ( )	(b) 152 × ( ) = ( )
(c) 175 × ( ) = ( )	(d) 109 × ( ) = ( )

Question Sheet	
(a) 133 × ( ) = ( )	(b) 177 × ( ) = ( )
(c) 164 × ( ) = ( )	(d) 192 × ( ) = ( )

Unit 6: Multiplication

Game (Pupil Textbook 3A, p 87)

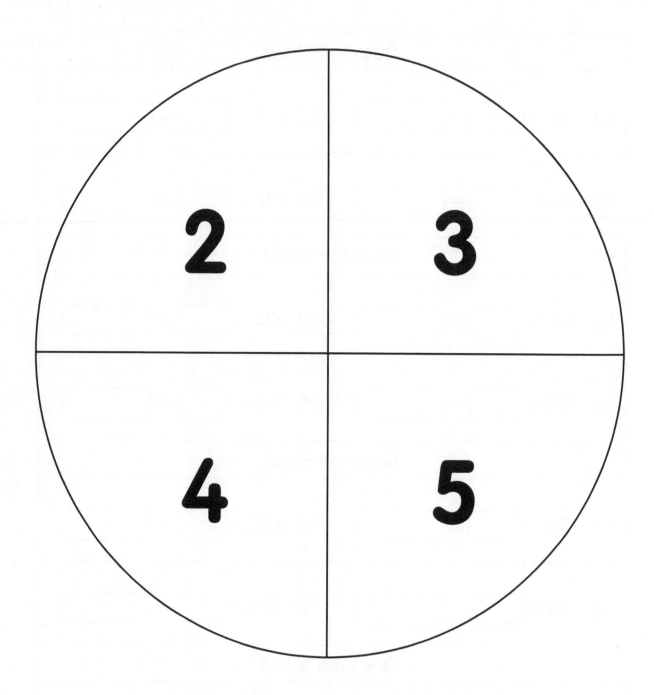